G000270392

A ROSE
BEYOND
THE
THAMES

A
ROSE
BEYOND
THE
THAMES

Michael
de Larrabeiti

THE BODLEY HEAD
LONDON SYDNEY
TORONTO

British Library Cataloguing
in Publication Data
De Larrabeiti, Michael
A rose beyond the Thames.
I. Title
823′.9′ 1F PR6054.E/
ISBN 0–370–30105–6

© Michael de Larrabeiti 1978
Printed and bound in Great Britain for
The Bodley Head Ltd
9 Bow Street, London WC2E 7AL
FILMSET ON APS 4/CCC in
Clowes Series 049, 11/13pt by
William Clowes and Sons Ltd, Beccles.
First published 1978

These things have been remembered as a child remembers, to make a story, true but not factual.
This book is dedicated
to Rose Leary and to no one else

Evening falls on the smoky walls,
   And the railings drip with rain,
And I will cross the old river
   To see my girl again.

The great and solemn-gliding tram,
   Love's still-mysterious car,
Has many a light of gold and white,
   And a single dark red star.

I know a garden in a street
   Which no one ever knew;
I know a rose beyond the Thames,
   Where flowers are pale and few.

Ballad of the Londoner: J. E. FLECKER

CONTENTS

THE
GREAT WAR

Rose must have gone like the wind up the dark slope of Wickersley Road, her hair flying, the long grey dress riding up between her knees as she ran, the chipped enamel jug in her right hand. Panting, she would have stopped on the edge of the crowded market, seeing the evening lit by the pale naphtha flares swinging on the stalls. Only a girl, slight and tough and wiry, she would have lowered her head and elbowed people's legs and thighs out of her way, making for the Beaufoy Arms to get the jug filled with mild. Outside the pub a man was fighting with his wife and she was screaming. Men gathered to watch, silent, uncritical. It happened every Saturday, no one interfered, except the girl. 'You bloody bully,' she shouted, pushing to the front of the crowd, 'leave her alone, can't yer?' The man did not break the rhythm of his swinging arm, he took a step and aimed a relaxed and drunken blow at the child's head. Often swiped, the girl ducked, expert, like a boxer, just an inch or two. The man's knuckles clanged against the jug and it sprang from the girl's hand and hit the brick wall of the pub; another chip in the enamel. The man didn't notice the pain and turned back to strike his wife. Rose stooped for the jug and went to get it filled.

She walked home slowly afterwards, careful not to spill a drop of beer and she told her father what had happened. She could tell him anything because they were friends. Ned would have shaken his head with great wisdom as he poured the dark ale, watching the weak bubbles rising to the brim. 'Never, ever, interfere with a couple who's quarrelling, whether you know 'em or you don't, it ain't worth it.'

Rose Leary was born in 1905, number eleven Wickersley Road, at the far end of Lavender Hill. She hated Battersea and spent most of her life trying to get away from it, but she never did. Strangely enough she often said that the Hill had been a good place to live, once; people in a street knew each other, used to sit out on the copings and shout backwards and forwards, 'Hey, where you off to then?' Rose knew hundreds of people.

She was the eldest of thirteen kids and it's difficult to be more unlucky than that. As soon as she could stand she began to help her mother with the work and there was no shortage of it. Gran was very hard and very strong and when she gave you a mouthful you knew it. She came from Camberwell, name of Champion, and her own father's mob was so rough that they once took the grid off a drain and shoved a copper down it head first. Gran is a little round old lady now and wouldn't hurt a fly, but she still finds it easy to hold her own in a slanging match.

I never knew my Grandad, Rose's father. His name was Ned Leary and he ran away from home to be a drummer boy in South Africa in the Boer War. He enjoyed himself so much that when it came to the Great War he didn't hesitate. He would have done if he'd known what was in store for him; his wife and kids left with nothing and Rose, his favourite child, going off with the first man who came along so that she could get out of Wickersley Road, out of Battersea.

On the first day of the Great War Ned Leary polished his boots in the kitchen. He was dark, handsome in the Irish way, with a moustache. He was very careful with his clothes and brushed them twice a day. He had one foot on a kitchen chair and he was wearing his best suit.

'Where are you going?' said Gran.

Ned Leary didn't look up but carried on cleaning his boots. 'To join up of course, woman, what else?'

What else indeed?

He wasn't away long before he came back wounded. He was put into Roehampton Hospital and they kept him there for months. Rose and her mother walked down the ward three times trying to recognise him. His hair had gone white, he looked fifty instead of thirty odd and he'd been away less than a year. The first thing he said was, 'Where'd you get that bloody silly hat, Becky?'

Gran had done her best to dress up for him.

Ned Leary had been advancing over no-man's land when a bullet hit him in the knee and smashed it. As he twisted and spun with the pain a dum-dum bullet exploded in his hip-bone and blew most of it away. He went down into the mud and stayed there for three days. He thought it was three days ... it might have been longer, or shorter.

He hated the French. 'They went by me, time after time, and left me groaning and begging for something to drink. I'd have died but for two Germans who found me and saw my rosary. They must have been Catholics too, God bless 'em. They pulled me to a ruin and gave me something to drink and eat. They couldn't take me out, it was raining bullets and shells outside. They came back a week later and got me before I died, just.'

He was sent to a German hospital and the nuns looked after him and cleaned him up. He came home a hero.

'Just look at the bloody mess I'm in,' he used to say when he'd had a drink. 'Look at the mess,' and he'd point at his leg. 'Sending us out to fight men who are the same as we are, risking their lives to save me, don't make sense. A cripple I am ... good men gone and good men going.'

As long as he lived, which wasn't long, he could only just walk with massive irons on his leg and a heavy boot on his foot with a sole five inches thick. He'd been so proud of his appearance. The shattered remains of the dum-dum bullet and the bits of bone in his hip never really healed properly and from time to time would break open into a gangrenous sore. On one of these occasions the panel doctor said it was 'flu, the infection was left too long and Ned died.

The funeral was extravagant. Ned's regiment, the East Surreys, sent a gun-carriage, a flag and some soldiers, and on the way to the cemetery the procession stopped outside every single pub. Everybody on Lavender Hill knew Ned because after the war, being unable to work, he'd become a bookie's runner and he'd spent his last few years out in the streets or inside the pubs. Gran didn't take too kindly to his long absences; she was extremely jealous and knew that Ned liked chancing his arm, and other parts of his anatomy as well. One day, when he was gazing deep down thoughtful into the tits of a plump barmaid, Gran rushed into the pub with his dinner on a dish and smacked it down in front of him so hard that the plate broke and the gravy ran over the counter and dripped to the floor.

'There's your fuckin' dinner,' she shouted, mad with anger, 'I'll bring your fuckin' bed up next.' Gran always swore a lot but then she had a lot to swear about.

Ned was particularly fond of Rose. She ran about the streets for him and carried his bets and messages, so they spent much of their time together. She once asked him what it was like to be drunk. He reached under the table and banged down a bottle of draught port and sat and drank it with her. She was about fourteen or fifteen. He had to carry her upstairs half an hour later and she was sick all over his jacket, but he laughed and put her carefully to bed and washed her face.

'It's not a good idea to drink too much in one go,' he said, 'but people do.'

Rose was Ned's messenger at twelve. With his bad leg Ned couldn't move very fast so Rose used to walk the streets with him and carry the betting slips. If the police appeared she would take to her heels, leaving Ned in the clear. Off-course betting was against the law so Ned needed to be artful. He worked for a Battersea bookie who lived in St Philip's Street and he was responsible for taking bets along the Hill, paying out the winnings and balancing the accounts with the bookie in the Craven public house every Saturday night.

Ned earned a good living from it because he was very popular and he was straight, only working in a 'skinner' when he was short of money. A 'skinner' was a winning bet that the runner wrote out for an accomplice after the race had been won. Ned and Nobby Clark, his neighbour, used to work together on skinners.

'Got a good winner today, Nobby?'

'Oh yes, very lucky,' Nobby would say and Ned would hand over the eleven quid or whatever it was. Later they'd meet and there'd be two quid for Nobby and nine for Ned.

The Clarks were good neighbours and friends for many years. Next door, the other way, it was different. Mrs Turner got drunk every Saturday and used to roll about in the road. It was a regular show and the kids got out of bed and ran to the windows to watch it. First she lay on her back kicking her heels in the air and slapping the ground with her hands, then she raised her legs and pulled her skirt above her head to show brilliant red bloomers. After this she cried a little and sat up, rocking herself sideways, quietly moaning, not noticing the kids laughing and pointing. 'I'm a one-man woman,' she'd say, 'always have been, I'm a one-man woman, always have been. I'm a one-man woman ...' Her husband had been killed in the trenches and she was living with a man who was called her cousin but the whole street knew otherwise and it preyed on her mind.

Ned had terrible trouble with the police because he did more business than any other bookie in Battersea. He would probably have set up on his own if he'd lived longer. Detective Constable Logan was the enemy and he tried hard to get Ned, but never managed it. Ned always knew somehow when Logan was on the prowl and by the time the law arrived on the scene Ned's money and betting slips were miles away in Rose's shopping basket. There was no catching her. She could run like a tram and all the stall-holders in the market knew her and she'd be reading a Sexton Blake comic under a vegetable barrow before Logan had grabbed Ned's collar.

Logan lived on the Hill too, Taybridge Road, and that's why they called him the Taybridge Disaster. He wore snappy suits and a white boater with a striped ribbon round it. He was a bully and swore to get Ned, and one day he nearly did.

Ned and Rose were indoors doing the books when someone rushed by and shouted, 'Logan's coming, Logan's coming.'

Ned went pale. The money and the slips were all

over the table and he didn't have much time. There was just one hiding place and Rose scooped everything up and went there.

Ned reached the front door as Logan came up the steps. 'I've got you this time, Leary,' Logan said, prodding with his finger. 'You've got the biggest book on the Hill and I'm going to get it.'

Ned stood by the door and Logan got him by the lapels and shook him. Poor old Ned, with one foot hardly touching the ground, even with the irons and the five-inch sole.

'Come on, Leary, where's the slips?'

'There ain't no slips, Logan, see for yourself. I ain't no runner. How can you have a one-legged bookie's runner? I'd have to hop.'

Logan had two other coppers with him and they tore the house apart.

'I hope you got a warrant, Logan, Becky will go mad if you make a mess.'

'I don't need a warrant for you, Leary.'

'I wish we'd had you in the trenches for half a day, Logan, we knew what to do with bastards like you, you'd have had a bullet in the back.'

Logan looked high and low. Rose's brothers and sisters clustered round the policemen, enjoying the watching. Logan even poked around the back yard and heaved up a paving-stone or two, but he found nothing. At the very last he pulled open the toilet door and there was Rose, legs dangling, heels banging. The smell was awful.

'Ooooff!' said Logan. 'Strike a light.'

'Piss off can't yer?' said Rose and leant forward and shut the door.

Logan went then. 'I'll get you, Leary, see if I don't,' he said and he stamped off down the street.

Ned rested his back against the front door and
grinned at his kids. Then he went out into the garden
and waited for Rose to emerge from the brick-built
lavatory which had a plank door with a little diamond
shape cut into it.

'You did well, girl,' he said in his soft voice, with just
the touch of Irish. 'How'd you turn on a smell to order?'

'Oh Dad,' she said, 'it was easy, I was so scared.'

Those outside lavatories had large wooden seats
screwed down with brass screws and scrubbed white.
The screws in the Learys' toilet were only finger-tight
and the seat could be lifted up and away in a trice.
That's where the betting slips were, and the money.

Rose also earned a few coppers by collecting horse-
dung and selling it to people for their gardens and
window-boxes. The trams were pulled by horses then,
with an extra one hitched on to get up Cedar's Road,
which is very steep and runs from the Common down
to Lavender Hill at the opposite end to Clapham
Junction.

I can just see Rose, a scraggy girl with a knowing
face, following horse-trams up and down Lavender
Hill, watching, waiting until a helpful horse drops a
load. There's the sound, there's the smell. The tram
moves off and with streaks of hair blowing across her
face, and under her dress the skinny knees mauve with
cold, Rose steps into the road, feeling that the whole
world is looking at her. She stops by the warm steaming
dollop; it looks platted, woven neatly like the dough of
a Jewish loaf. She bends and slides the broad blade of
the coal-shovel underneath the brown straw-flecked
horse-shit, trying not to break its wholeness. She fails
and it falls apart, her shovel scrapes the tarmac.

A full load is heavy and as Rose walks she levers the

bucket along on her thigh, the metal handle cutting into the crook of her arm. And, with her nostrils breathing at the unexpected country smell, she swings her way up to the posher houses facing the Common, to sell manure from door to door.

One day Rose found a great rich dollop of the stuff at the bottom of Altenburg Gardens and was just pushing it into a pile when she looked up and was terrified to see, coming towards her at a stately lick, a baker's cart, and sitting high up, like a prince, was Albie Clark. Albie Clark lived next door and was the boy that Rose doted on. She scraped up what remained of the muck and, keeping her face well down, she scooted into an alley that opened up to her right. She stood there, concealed, bucket in one hand and the wooden-hafted coal-shovel in the other, safe from discovery and shame. Safe that was until the horse and cart swerved into that very alley and rattled over the cobbles. She had taken refuge in the bakery entrance.

'I always feel guilty when I see horse-manure, even after all these years,' Rose says when you're out with her and she sees some. 'I'm really glad the motor-car's taken over.'

Being neighbours the Learys and the Clarks had their lavatories back to back in the yard and these little sheds shared a common wall. Rose and Albie loosened a brick there and left notes and presents for each other underneath it. Sometimes the betting slips passed from one lavatory to the other, especially when Logan was out and about.

Rose was sure she loved Albie, but they were soon separated. When Ned died she was sent into service and she never saw Albie again. By and by she heard that he had gone into the building trade and become rich. Her soft spot for Albie lasted years. I saw her meet someone out shopping on the Hill once, someone who knew Albie, and Rose said, 'Oh really, how's he doing? Oh really, that's nice,' and the tiredness dropped from her and for a moment I saw a skinny girl collecting manure again along Lavender Hill.

Ned Leary must have been, in his own way, a wise man with a lot of tenderness in him. During the First World War men were given white feathers for cowardice if it was thought that they should have been fighting in the trenches instead of loafing around the pubs. The feathers were always handed out by women, to make the men feel cheap and cowardly.

One day Ned was sitting in the Craven, he'd just paid over his money to the bookie, and was drinking his beer. The place was crowded, it was a Saturday, noisy and busy. A young woman stepped in at the door, a white feather in her hand, and the pub went quiet, gradually, until there wasn't a sound except what came from the streets outside.

Ned was sitting behind the table on which he'd done his books. His legs weren't visible and the woman chose him and walked all the way down the bar and put the feather on the table where Ned sat alone. He was wearing his cap and she wouldn't have been able to see his white hair. Ned didn't say a word but finished his drink, picked up the feather, reached over for his stick and edged his way out.

Every man in that pub put down his glass and watched that woman as she tried to say sorry to Ned. He smiled at her and patted her on the shoulder. 'If you knew what it was like, girl,' he said, 'you'd lay down your life to stop 'em sending good men out there to be made into old cripples like me, before their time,' and he limped from the pub and went home.

Only Rose was indoors and she watched him sitting

silently by the black grate for half an hour before she realised that tears were running down his cheeks. Ned told her what had happened though he never mentioned it to anyone else.

'Bloody fool,' he said time after time as he sat there, 'bloody fool.' Rose never knew if he meant the woman who had given him the white feather or himself for going to the war in the first place.

So Ned died and Rose became a domestic servant, it was that or the laundry. Her exciting free life with her father had gone. To replace it came years of dullness and work, a storing up of dullness. That was to be Rose's life as it became distinct from Ned's.

Rose set off into the country with a small trunk, waved away from Clapham Junction station by her mother and her brothers and sisters. Apart from the old butler trying to get her horizontal all the time and feeling her with his pork-sausage fingers, her job wasn't too bad. She was the nursery maid and allowed to have the same lessons as the children of the house. She discovered that she was bright and in fact could be brighter than her superiors, but then her wits had been sharpened on the Battersea grindstone, sharpened so as to be lethal. The lady of the house taught Rose the social graces, like it was vulgar to whistle and to run, but what was the good of that with the old dullness still waiting for her, just round the corner?

The call soon came from Wickersley Road and Rose hurried home. Gran needed her badly; she was ironing all day at the laundry, feeding the family and also trying to keep Ned's book while her son John sponged a living by slipping in skinners every day. Rose moved back to number eleven, found a job as a waitress in the Strand Corner House and ran her feet raw for a couple of years, skivvying and helping her mother bring up the children. It was a hopeless existence and not surprising that she ran away from it as soon as she could, only to exchange what she had for more of the same.

My Old Man was born with the gift of the gab in one hand and the way of the world in the other. He moved through the West End easily, like a magician. He wore dark overcoats and dark Homburg hats. His shoes were new and always highly polished and he never had holes in his socks. He was a smart operator who lived from doing a bit of this and a bit of that. A deal here, a deal there, and you were set up for a twelve-month. The Old Man was good at it too, a bit of a crawler but an enthusiastic one. He could talk to people and make them listen.

Rose served him coffee one night in the Corner House and their lives came together and mixed. He had his feet up on a chair, reading a newspaper and smoking. Rose pulled the chair away, banged down the cup and saucer and told him he had no manners. Night after night the Old Man followed her home after work and wouldn't stop following her until she gave in. Rose was seventeen, he was twenty-eight.

They moved into a nice flat in a mews at the top of Cedar's Road and they must have got on to start with because she had three children by the time she was twenty-one. But whatever there was between them began to disappear and the Old Man with it. The disappearing trick was his speciality; a day, a night, a month, a year, it was all the same to him, abracadabra.

He could reappear at will too, over garden walls, through windows, leading a dance of bailiffs behind him sometimes. Rose found it impossible to put up with the uncertain demands the Old Man made on her body, her feelings, and she tried to give him the slip, moonlight-flitting all over London and even out into the country. Her attempts failed. The Old Man was moody, jealous, suspicious, handy with his fists. He became his own private detective and snooper. Rose was easy to find, she couldn't go far or fast with three children and she wouldn't leave them. She had to settle for what she'd got, a life of hard work, bringing up the kids on her own and by her own efforts, seeing the Old Man only when he was broke and could tear himself away from the West End.

So she left Cedar's Road, which was too expensive, and began a never-ending gypsy trek in search of ever cheaper lodgings. She tried to find work outside the city so that her three boys could have 'healthy fresh air', but she ended up in the cheapest place in the borough, in the buildings at the end of Battersea High Street, right by the river, where the smell from Price's candle factory made you sick.

We lived in Eaton House, 23, and Gran, who had left Wickersley at last, had moved into Archer House. I was about three years old then, a fourth boy, the result of a short truce between Rose and the Old Man.

They told me I'd been born in the maternity ward of St Thomas's Hospital but I knew better. I could remember stepping alive from the walls of Eaton House, straight into the smell of Battersea Reach. There was a damp tunnel of dripping bricks; it connected the two blocks of buildings and I came out of it and I was screaming and running for my Gran.

The way she tells it I came roaring to her that some hooligan was killing my eldest brother, Steve. Gran leapt out of her kitchen like a flapping-track greyhound, grabbed her umbrella, put her hand on her hat and galloped through the arches with murder blazing on her face. When we found Steve he was on the ground astride a kid of about his own age and smashing the living daylights out of him. This kid had roller-skates on and couldn't get up. He was like that my brother Steve, never took a chance when it came to fighting.

'You fuckin' little git,' Gran shouted at Steve and walloped him across the shoulders with her brolly. 'You effin' little bully, leave him alone.'

Steve was up and away in a flash and ran into the High Street. The other kid sat up and started crying, his nose was bleeding. Gran whacked him over the head with the umbrella. 'Shut up whining, yer great pansy,' she said. Then she turned round and in the same movement caught me one across the head with the back of her hand. 'And that's for bringing me out on a wild goose chase,' and she stalked off through the tunnel, back to Archer House and her cooking.

My brothers enjoyed living down in the High Street because when they got out of school, if they'd bothered to go, they ran free. The long tunnels and balconies of the buildings, the railway embankments and the river's edge by St Mary's and Ransome's dock, that was their world. There was the street market too, where, if he was hungry and it seemed miles until teatime, a kid could always steal an apple or an orange.

Gran couldn't give eye to them much because she was at work every day until five o'clock, so my brothers frequently found their share of trouble, more than their share sometimes. Rose often came home from work, tired, to get the tea, and found a policeman looking for the boys because they'd stolen something; or a neighbour banged on the door to complain about her beaten up son or a daughter's knickers, lost. There was always a row, with the boys watching from the hallway, and Rose would end it saying, 'Well, if your kids ain't got the sense to stand the right way up, keep 'em indoors,' and she'd slam the door.

One day, end of the week, Friday, she saw her three eldest rushing down the High Street towards her. They were waving two pairs of socks in one hand and underpants and handkerchieves in the other. She thought they'd been thieving and were running away.

My brothers already had names of course but it happened that their school, the nearest to the buildings, was Trott Street, which was, and still is, a Catholic school. 'Have you been baptised?' they were asked one day. 'No,' they said. Rose had never had the time to have them done. The nuns and priests went berserk. 'What!' they shouted. 'But this is terrible, we'll have to do you right away, immediately, you could be run over on the way home and go to hell.' My brothers thought this was fine. It was better than lessons or catechism.

'Right,' said the nuns, 'what are your names?' and the boys told them: Steve, George, Tim. One name was not enough for the nuns and my brothers were each allowed to choose two more names on their own, which is a gift not often given to children. The names they chose were not suitable of course and the nuns insisted they take saints' names. At last the priest was called and the boys were 'done' properly and according to the rules and given presents to commemorate the day. This made them very excited and they ran off to Prince's Head to meet Rose from work, shouting as soon as they saw her pushing her way through the crowds behind the barrows.

Rose had carried her shopping, and me, from the day nursery at Parkgate Road and her legs ached, but she heard the boys from halfway down the street.

'I'm Steven Bernard Sebastian.'

'I'm George Francis Eustace.'

'I'm Timothy Aloysius Antony.'

Rose just stood there, rooted to the pavement for an instant, her arms full of shopping and child, people pushing past her to get home. I looked closely into her face. She was still a girl and her laughter made everyone around her laugh, it was warm, folded you up like an arm, strong. Her voice was rounded at the edges, rounded by kindness. I knew all this because I was perched near her shoulder, my feet amongst her shopping bags.

Rose laughed again and the circles of people within earshot looked at us and laughed too.

'Well,' she said, 'at least you got some socks and things out of it.' Then she shifted her grip on me and let me slide down the side of her body till I stood with my brothers on the pavement.

WORLD
WAR TWO

My Ma put me right down onto the pavement and into the Second World War. The next day, it seemed, I was hoisted out of the family and with a faceful of tears and a label round my neck I was sent by train to Arundel in Sussex, sitting in the guard's van like a carrier pigeon in a crate. I was delivered to a semi-detached house in Maxwell road to live with a lady they called Aunt Vicky and her husband Colin. He wasn't well enough to be called up and he drove a bread van for the Co-op instead. Suddenly my Ma was no longer near at hand and I knew what being on my own meant and I was scared. The war was nothing by comparison. This new house threatened me with its cleanliness, it smelt of an antagonistic polish and there was a clock in the hall that ticked loud and leisurely, chiming at every quarter to remind me of the slowness of time away from London. Within a day or two I was beaten for taking the knickers off a four-year-old girl in the recreation ground, behind a tree. I'd taken my trousers down as well but it was no good explaining. Off came my trousers again and I got a hiding, the first of many.

The war was not the sole cause of my being sent away. Ma had been caught stealing at work and it had seemed for a while that there would be no one to look after me. One of my aunts had married an Arundel man and it was he who arranged for me to be sent to relations of his. Ma was let off when the magistrate

heard about her children but the war had been declared
meanwhile and I was left down in Sussex for safety.
Everyone was convinced that the Germans would
bomb the capital flat within a week and kids were
being shipped out of London like it had the plague.

I hated being evacuated, I was missing everything.
The war was exciting but it was happening in London,
not in Arundel. Everything was wrong. I was separated
from my brothers and I was lonely. I was in a new
school and Aunt Vicky had no children of her own,
a disadvantage. I had the benefit of all her attention,
and Colin's. Worse, they had no experience of the
keeping of a little savage like me. I'm surprised I
didn't get meningitis. 'Do this, do that ... wash your
hands ... don't touch those ... you can't have this if you
don't eat that ... look how dirty your clothes are, your
hands are filthy.' They didn't understand about dirt,
how the whole world is covered with the stuff, made
from it.

Right at the beginning of my exile two of my uncles
made a foray to Arundel to rescue me for a few hours.
They brought me a whiff of London and reminded me
that real life was still going on. I was standing after
breakfast in the bay window and gazing with hatred at
the other side of the road, when two men, one carrying
a suitcase, walked to the front door. I'd watched them
come up from the bus-stop at the bottom of the hill.
They were big men, bearing a vast weight of knowledge
and self-confidence with them, and they bore it effort-
lessly. They smiled all the time, and nothing, nothing
at all, took them off balance. They could handle
anything, anybody.

They could handle Vicky all right; she was a blushing
bundle of embarrassment two seconds after she'd opened
the front door.

'We've come to take Mick out for the day,' said Uncle Den.

'Yes,' said Uncle Ned. He'd been named for my grandfather and had the same charm. 'Perhaps you'd like to come too? A walk in the park could change a person's life.'

'Ooh,' said Vicky. 'You must come in . . . a cup of tea? Have you come straight from the station?'

'We stopped for . . . mm . . . breakfast,' lied Ned, touching a thin and untrustworthy moustache, 'in a public house.'

'Public house,' Vicky giggled. The very idea!

Dennis gave her the suitcase he was carrying. We never saw a lot of the Old Man but, during the war, we were never short of butter, sugar, jam, chocolate and bacon. We never asked him where it came from, we ate it.

'Here's some stuff to keep you healthy,' said Dennis. 'But you look well enough, don't she Ned?'

'My word yes,' said Ned and ogled Vicky and she gave herself over to his control, mind and body.

I'd never seen anything like it. Such mastery. Here was a trade worth learning.

My uncles had me out of the house in a second, free for the day, a good late summery day of the phoney war. It was lunch at the Norfolk Arms with Den and Ned down from Battersea on my mother's money, pretending to be landed gentlemen with landed accents, making me fall off my chair with laughter. They charmed waiters and waitresses alike, getting them to do the most extraordinary things, tempting them to join in the day's enjoyment, forcing them to forget they were working, to forget the war. Two adults giving a day over to a child, and in that day there was nothing more important than the giving of it.

'The boats have all been booked,' said the old lady when Ned and Dennis tried to take me on the river after the meal. 'Most of them have been laid up.'

Dennis and Ned weren't a bit perturbed. Dennis shoved his hands deep into his pockets and looked at the disappointment on my face and decided the world had to change then and there. Ned squinted at the sun and looked thunderstruck. He took the lady aside, avuncular, by the elbow. She was twice his age.

'All the way from London,' I heard him whisper. 'His father's in the RAF, you know what that means? Mother's gone, we're all he's got really, got to go back, tonight, our regiments . . .'

No money changed hands; what did they need with money when they always got their own way? The old lady opened a shed and we dragged out a long and lovely wooden craft. There was a rudder, operated by two yards of rope, and a high carved trellis round the stern. Down the River Arun we went with me in the front, trailing my hands in the weed-green water, spearing the fish with my eyes.

Uncle Ned leant forward to the oars, his face beautiful, serene, handsome, cunning, dabs of light danced across it, reflected from the river. He pulled an inch of white shirt-cuff beyond each sleeve of his brown sports-coat and the sun shone there. I'd never seen it done before and it showed me something more than shirt. Ned looked at my puzzled face and said, 'I always like to show a little bit of cuff, Mick, not too much, just enough. Never overdo things, eh?'

'You've got to be crafty,' said Dennis, and then, 'Watch out, Mick, submarines everywhere, waiting to sink us; keep your eyes open, and sing out when you see one.'

We didn't go far, just to the Black Rabbit Inn on the

bank of the river by the chalk quarry. Den and Ned sat on a wooden bench and drank from brown bottles and smiled at me and the trees, and everything dropped into place, quietly, as the sun went down.

They went home that evening on the train and I didn't see them again till after the war, and I was lucky to do that. I thought I would cry my heart out when they left me back at Aunt Vicky's with secret hoards of money in my pockets. They told me to hide the cash but they never told me that my mother had sent it.

All my uncles, and I had lots of them, were rascals, candid and careless. My mother's sisters, my mother often said it, had each married a layabout with no style. Her brothers were different, even I as a five-year-old could see that. They were coloured butterflies, not plain cabbage whites. For the first time in my life, that day in Arundel, I was made aware of the free-wheeling fellowship which my uncles and their confederates had formed to protect themselves from the demands life might make upon them. They used women shamelessly, and women, even the Aunt Vickys of this world, recognised the secret society of the men and smiled at it, conspired with it, allowing it to exist. The Uncle Neds have talent, cunning and charm; they whistle silently through their teeth, borrow another quid from mother, sister or girl-friend, and life goes on. An inch of cuff, a gesture, a phrase and a child moves a step into the frightening world of the grown-up. It was like hearing an unusual noise at night and crossing the darkness of the bedroom to look into the burning spot of light at the keyhole and for the first time seeing the bright bodies together. The mystery is solved and made more mysterious in the one instant. That night I rushed to the safety of my bed open-eyed, and I pondered on the magic of Uncle Den and Uncle Ned.

It was different when my mother came to see me. Her visits made me cry. As soon as she'd got over the trouble with the magistrates she took the train to Arundel once a month and I would cling to her for a day, begging her to take me home.

'Aunt Vicky is very fond of you really, Mick,' she would say. 'It's for your own good you know, you'll just have to behave, that's all.' But I yearned for London, I wanted to be where I belonged when the Germans landed.

Some time in October 1939 my brothers were evacuated to Reading. There was nowhere for them to go at first and they were shunted from house to house. Nobody wanted the three of them together, they weren't Fauntleroys, even my Ma had to admit that, and it was difficult to get them settled.

There were some people at the beginning of the war who took in as many evacuees as they could, simply to qualify for the subsistence money. If they could feed and house the kids on next to nothing any money they had left over was theirs. My brothers had been carried off at last by an old crone who had a house with so many evacuees in it that they were falling out of the windows and she was making a good living. There was no heating, my brothers ate their meals with their overcoats on, and slept together in the same bed, sideways like pilchards in a tin. There were huge spuds in the heels of their socks and their feet were black and their toes were encrusted together with the yellow pus which had oozed from broken chilblains and dried, making each foot look like a shallow dish of toad-in-the-hole with five sausages in it. They were cold all the time too and their faces were plastered with elasticated snot. The house was a Fagin's kitchen, Ma said. She brought the boys home on the first train and sent the three of them down to Arundel to be near me.

I accepted Arundel once my brothers were in the town. It wasn't like living in London and I didn't see them every day but I knew they were there. Steve wasn't to stay long, he was due to leave school any time, but he stayed long enough. The war between the local kids and the London foreigners was settled soon after his arrival and my brothers' London gang ruled with no one to oppose them. It meant that I was a princeling during my entire stay in Arundel. No Sussex kid dared touch me for fear of a heavy and sudden revenge. My brothers never lost one fight while they were evacuated and they never let the locals get us down, outnumbered or not.

The moment the boys arrived in Arundel they began to plan their escape, but they planned astutely, knowing that they needed lots of money before they could get away and stay away. Steve had the ideas, the schemes and the tricks, George manipulated the money, buying and selling, and Tim was henchman and scout, up to everything, a good thief, a good runner. Each one of them was essential to the central plot but not one of them could have achieved anything on his own. Steve was far too careless, George too selfish and Tim too active.

It all began with the bike factory. During the war most private cars were taken off the road and bikes became very precious. The boys ransacked Sussex for every scrap of bicycle they could find. They snooped around dumps and old garden sheds until they had an enormous collection of buckled wheels, patched tyres, bent frames and rusty mudguards. From the bits they had collected they made new bikes, bikes that only hung together long enough to be sold.

All went well until my brothers had the bad luck to sell their dodgiest bike to a classmate, a policeman's son and so beyond consideration. But even my brothers could not have expected the boy to ride the machine down Castle Street, a hill as steep as a brick wall and certain death for the over-confident. He didn't stand a chance. Both his wheels were buckled and clanged dangerously against the forks, front and rear. When the bike moved at speed it reared and swayed unpredictably, like an unbroken horse. As soon as the boy squeezed the brakes the metal rods which worked the system pulled themselves away from the nuts that were meant to hold them in position. In less than three seconds the policeman's son was pitching down the hill, stiff-armed with fear, completely out of control, at thirty miles an hour. The back wheel collapsed and the bike slithered, horizontal, pushing the screaming boy along before it. Luckily it disintegrated and, incapable of anything else, stopped just a yard or two away from the front wheels of a double-decker bus that was swinging wide to enter Tarrant Street. The boy, grazed down both legs, hands and one shoulder, was carried away in an ambulance to the Cottage Hospital and the bike was swept into a couple of biscuit tins. That evening the bicycle factory was closed, by the law.

Whatever the setbacks though, the Great Escape Fund had to go on, and Steve put his brain to work. One of the grocer's shops in Arundel was run by an old man who could hardly see. There was also a small and unguarded museum and Tim was a collector of things who did not care much where they came from. These facts met in Steve's head and a fool-proof scheme was the result.

Tim began his collection of foreign coins with a selection stolen from the local museum and Steve commandeered all those that looked like two-bob bits and half-crowns. Steve began to borrow me from Aunt Vicky on Saturday mornings, when the shops were busy, and fitting me out with a shopping bag, a shopping list and a handful of coins, he shoved me into the blind grocer's convinced that my innocent face, my tender years, would completely disarm the grocer even if he spotted the coins. He never did; how could anyone suspect such a lovely little boy of passing dud money?

The thing that amazed us about these transactions was not the exchange of useless coins for valuable goods, which George later sold on the open market, it wasn't that at all. It was the fact that we got real change into the bargin, a bonus of spendable money; that was sheer conjuring. Another benefit we hadn't looked for was a rise in Aunt Dolly's esteem. Aunt Dolly, a relative of Vicky's, had taken my three brothers into her neat home with its trim garden and regretted it immediately. Nothing could save those boys! Now suddenly they were taking an interest in collecting foreign coins and Aunt Dolly emptied all her drawers and canvassed all her friends. Foreign coins came showering down and for a while we went into the blind man's shop every day. But it wasn't enough, the Great Escape Fund needed more.

Though hailing from Battersea the boys were not slow to pick up country ways. Meat was on the ration and rabbits and pheasants fetched a very good price on the black market, any food did. My brothers soon turned the haphazard scrumping of local kids into well-organised market gardening.

The land surrounding Arundel belonged to the Duke of Norfolk and my sense of geography, as well as of fairness, was outraged by his possession of vast lands in Sussex. Why didn't he stay where he belonged?

It was a very fine estate with parkland, woods, streams and stately farms. This countryside was rich in apples, cob-nuts, blackberries, gooseberries and game of all kinds. Steve determined to put the produce of the land to the service of the fund.

I went on most of his rabbit hunts, not because I was a help, in fact I was much too small, but because Aunt Vicky had a fox-terrier with a dash of lurcher in it. Patch was his name and he was a killer, murdering anything that moved on the Norfolk acres.

Steve, with George and Tim, would cycle down to Maxwell Road and knock on our door. Aunt Vicky would smile at the dirty honest faces, the spikes of uncombed hair.

'Oh hello, Aunt Vicky. Aunt Dolly thought it would be a nice day to take little Mickie out for a ride.'

She fell for it every time.

'Well, that is nice ... You could take Patch with you, he never gets a good long run these days.'

Patch knew what was going on even if Vicky didn't. He wagged his tail till it fell off.

They got my fairy-cycle from the garden shed and with Patch running and barking alongside I would pedal behind my brothers as fast as I could, my short legs churning till they blurred. As soon as we got out of Vicky's sight they dumped my bike behind a hedge, taking it in turns to carry me on their cross-bars, for there was a long journey ahead.

We went miles, down Long Mill Road, over the bridge, past the park and into the woods beyond the Black Rabbit. The bikes were hidden and I was given a paratrooper's spade and told to follow as best I might. My brothers ranged ahead with the dog.

Sooner or later Patch would find a rabbit dozing in a clump of grass or snoozing behind a tree and very

often the dog would jump his quarry there and then.
At other times that rabbit would be off to a good start
and he'd go to ground and the spade was called for. I
used to turn in muddy circles for hours, seeing no
horizon, lost in jungles of grass twice as tall as I was,
guided only by the shouts and whistles of my brothers,
angry in the distance: 'Over here with that bloody
spade, where is he? We should never have brought him.'

When I arrived at the warren it was to see Patch's
behind sticking out of one hole while Steve, George
and Tim blocked off all the others. They took the spade
from me with a snatch and dug the rabbit out while I
kept watch for farmers and gamekeepers, lying on the
ground, smelling the cold in the grass and the damp
coming out of the broken earth. At last the rabbit,
writhing and scratching, was pulled into the grey
daylight to meet death. They held it up by the legs and
even with its body twisting away from the blow they
bashed it behind the head with the spade, and, still
warm, its fur soft and wonderful to the touch, it was slit
open with a penknife and paunched and the corpse
was bundled into a bag which I was given to carry. We
could pick up as many as five or six most days and at
three or four shillings each it was good money. My
brothers occasionally gave me sixpence to make me feel
part of the business and, I suspect, to buy my silence,
though they had that for nothing.

We caught pheasants too in a manner that was taught
to us by the Arundel schoolboys. It was easier to take
pheasant than rabbit because they were almost tame
and were hand-reared by the landowners for their sport.
We used to steal a handful of raisins and fix them onto
each point of an everywhichway fish-hook. Pheasants
love raisins and they'd jump on them without any
hesitation at all and swallow them down in a mouthful.

Our fish-hook was attached to a long length of strong twine and once it hit the pheasant's stomach we'd drag him in while he struggled and flapped like a big fish and hold him down to the ground and smash his head off with the spade. It was easy work and pheasant always fetched a good price. People were more than happy to get the extra meat and though they knew very well where we got it from we were never given away. We always took care in avoiding the gamekeepers who patrolled the Duke of Norfolk's estate, though one day we were nearly caught and transportation to the colonies seemed only a sneeze away.

We were in thick woods halfway up the steep side of a valley and I was hanging onto a tree that grew sideways out into the thin air, keeping a watch on the path which ran along the bottom, by a stream. Suddenly, at the far end I saw a gamekeeper, strolling along like the Duke of Norfolk himself. I knew he was wearing a Norfolk jacket, which I thought was something to do with the Duke and the Duke's service. His cap was tweed and very smart and his gaiters shone a deep nutty brown and reflected the cold light. Most frightening was the polished steel of the double-barrelled shot-gun that drooped from the crook of his arm. Somewhere in my mind was the idea that if you were caught in the act of poaching you could be shot out of hand by a gamekeeper, like shooting burglars in your bedroom. The man came on. I crawled up the tree a yard or so to where my brothers were digging out a rabbit, noisily. I touched them and they looked down into the valley. The blood drained from their eyes and they blinked with fear. There was no time to hide; the digging had cast a big brown scar of earth down the hillside and the scar pointed upwards like an arrowhead to where we squatted in the open, an easy shot. He could have picked us off like clay pipes at the fair. I took Patch in my arms and Steve stroked him and George held him round the mouth, but Patch had lurcher blood and his ancestors must have known all about gamekeepers, for he never made a sound.

The gamekeeper moved along the valley floor, his heels striking into the earth at an arrogant angle, his gun-barrels glinting. He looked up, he looked back, he looked sideways and he looked down, but somehow he never saw us, though he stopped near enough to spit on and changed his gun from one arm to the other, a moment when we all died. At last he went away and we fell back against the freshly dug earth and let our hot breath escape in trumpets of steam. We were silenced by the shock and held our hands over our eyes for a while to blot out the image of the horrible death we had escaped. It was not until years later that I realised the gamekeeper must have known all along that we were up there and what we were doing.

In the spring of 1940 Steve left school and left Arundel. My craftiest uncle, John, had found himself a reserve occupation, which meant he didn't have to join the army and spent his time painting aircraft hangars. Steve went off to work with him.

So Arundel became unbearable. I saw less and less of George and Tim and whatever schemes they had for the Great Escape Fund were kept to themselves. Evacuation became a drudgery. I began to forget what it was like to live in Battersea. I hated my mother for deserting me and loved her every time she came to see me. I tried everything I could think of to get her to take me back to London but it never worked. All I achieved was the triumph of making her cry and although that

gave me pleasure I always ended up weeping more
bitterly than she did.

She was now working as a caretaker in a huge house
in Pall Mall but to get the job she had told her
employers that she was a childless widow. If the lie
were discovered she would be dismissed with a week's
notice and nothing more. I felt lonely and unhappy but
I had to be content. There was a war on.

A few days after one of her visits that springtime I
was sitting at the tea-table and getting told off for not
eating my cauliflower, when suddenly there was a
commotion at the door. There were shouts and sobs in
the hallway and eventually Aunt Dolly burst into the
room, purple veins throbbing across her face, tears
hanging onto her nose. She poked her face close to
mine and gazed at me as if I were unreal. I was used to
local children doing this, but not adults. I gazed back at
her, defiant. What had happened? The Jerries must
have landed! Littlehampton had been captured! The
real news was far worse. The Great Escape Fund had
reached its target, George and Tim had followed Steve
into the big world. They had done a bunk.

The money they had saved over the months must
have come to an enormous sum, enough to keep them
in luxury for the rest of their lives. They'd kept it
under the floor of the garden shed. Just a day or two
before leaving they'd sold their own bikes for a king's
ransom and unloaded every foreign coin they could
muster onto the half-blind grocer. Aunt Dolly's eyes
became shifty with shame as she told us of the man
coming to her with a tin full of useless coins and
shaking it under her nose like a persistent beggar.

On the eve of their departure George and Tim had
gone to bed early and then, rising before the rest of the
household, they had caught the first train to London,

looking like young scholars in their shop-lifted Jaeger suits. The only sign of their going was the wallpaper in their bedroom. It hadn't been properly pasted into the angles and there was a lot of air trapped behind it in corners. Tim had been beaten often for popping the paper with his finger but before leaving he had popped the whole lot and, worse, he'd run his finger down to join all the pop-holes together. Tim had a fine sense of revenge.

The boys' teacher came to the house but there was nothing to be done. He was sure that they had gone home to London and he wasn't a bit worried. 'Those boys can look after themselves better than we can,' he said. 'The thing now is to keep your eye on this one.'

Dolly and Vicky gave me a pair of old-fashioned looks and put me to bed with many kind words, but kind words were not enough. I knew all my brothers were gone now and I dreamt and fought with a fearsome nightmare of a green dragon that pursued me down an endless yellow field, capturing me in huge tree-roots that rolled like a python and held me tight. My hatred of Arundel grew. I was followed everywhere. I was met and taken to school. The teachers on playground duty stood by the gate and kept me in sight all the time. I fretted and schemed, I became intent and sly. I could get money as well as my brothers could. I had the dog, I could go scrumping, and I knew the outlets for anything I could steal. No, the real problem was that I could never get past the railway ticket office. A five-year-old would not be allowed to travel on his own, not unless he was put on the train by an adult. I plotted and I swore but I saw no escape. I became morose and miserable.

The war went on. The heavy air-raids began in London and bombs fell all over the country too as the

German raiders unloaded high explosives that they had not been able to use on the capital. Being between the coast and a fighter aerodrome I saw many a dog-fight between Spitfires and Messerschmitts. These battles became so frequent that I soon learnt to distinguish German planes from British ones by engine noise alone. 'It's one of ours,' I could reassure Vicky when she came to comfort me in the dark of my bedroom in the middle of the night.

As the Battle of Britain became more violent the dog-fights increased, the RAF trying to stop the Germans getting to London in the first place, and then trying to prevent them getting home once the raid was over. I will never forget the feelings of deep sadness I experienced when our planes went down in flames and no parachute fell. I can remember too the pride and hatred such battles nourished in me, like the day the sky sparkled blue high up and two silver fighters went round and round, chasing one another for their lives in the sunlight, the noise of their engines slicing across the square emptiness and over the roofs of the town.

The siren had gone but there was no real danger and everyone was out in Tarrant Street as usual. I was on my own for once, sent to get the papers and my weekly Mickey Mouse comic. Everything in the town had come to a standstill. The buses, the few cars, the bicycles, had all stopped and drivers and passengers were in the streets, pointing. Some were walking backwards in circles with their noses poking to the sky, following the two beautiful planes with their eyes as they swooped at each other, coming lower and lower until we could see the markings on their wings.

The policeman in Tarrant Street made no attempt to move us on and all was quiet there except for that hard noise of the engines. Round, climb, turn and twist,

bank and fall; then the Spit got in behind the Jerry and
you could feel the pilot's thumb on the button and
everyone in the town gave a vicious jerk of the shoulders
and said, 'Go on, give it 'im, give it to 'im, the swine.'
And out came the sound of the cannon, dah-dah-dah-
dah-dah-dah-dah-dah-dah-dah.

The Messerschmitt spun, faltered, but it was too late.
He lost speed and the Spit peeled away to make sure
there was no one on his tail, then came back to watch.
Smoke began to pour from the 109, a wisp at first, then
thickly. The German pilot pushed back the canopy of
the cockpit and rolled out onto the open air, and there
he was, the enemy, at the end of a white parachute,
floating, swinging, powerless.

The silence in the street broke and a great cheer
went up. People smiled and brushed tears from their
eyes and slapped each other on the back and stamped
their feet.

'Got 'im,' they said. 'That's the way, we'll soon send
the bastards packing, that's the only way to deal with
them, the only language they understand,' and they
laughed.

The Spit went round the parachute a couple of
times, did a victory roll over the town and then flew
towards the airfield, and people walked away, excited,
knowing we would win the war in the end.

All the kids who had bikes, me included, pedalled off
in the direction of Arundel Park where, we estimated,
the parachute would land. There was only one way to
get there, between the castle and the river, but the
police had lost no time and were already blocking the
road when we arrived. I waited to see if they would let
us through but they didn't and so, hours late, I cycled
back to Maxwell Road. I didn't have Vicky's newspapers,
nor did I have my comic, and I expected what she

called a 'good spanking', but I told her what I had been doing and, miraculously, I wasn't punished.

'I know,' said Vicky, 'isn't it wonderful?' There was something marvellous for kids about the war, you could get away with murder.

We heard about the Jerry at school next day. They said he'd gone straight into Swanbourne Lake and when they'd got him out his legs had come off because he'd been machine-gunned right across his middle and he'd died soon afterwards. We all thought it was the best thing that could have happened; it made one less to kill later on.

But even this excitement couldn't compensate for not being in London and I became ill. My mother came down to look at me, decided that I was a 'bundle of nerves' and took me home with her. In the train I showed her all the money I'd saved and she saw that I was better already.

'What a bunch of kids I've got,' she said, and she was right.

Home had changed its place several times while I'd been away and now we lived right in the middle of the West End, at thirteen Carlton House Terrace. I arrived there at the peak of the Blitz and I saw, even in daytime, that the sky above London looked dirty and ashen, curling brown along the edges, scarred by the fires of the previous night, like a half-burned love-letter.

Carlton House Terrace was very close to St James's Park, at the top of the Duke of York's Steps, and the house we lived in was one of a large series of houses joined together on all levels and just made for a child to explore and enjoy. During the war number thirteen was taken over by the Red Cross, who stored food there and packed it into parcels to send to British prisoners in Germany, which meant that we didn't go short of a thing. We were convinced that most of the parcels were going straight into German stomachs anyway so we didn't feel we were doing wrong, and we never took more food than we needed. Ma was employed to keep the place clean and, on the nights when bombs were falling, it was also her job to run up to the roof and throw sand on anything she saw burning.

There were literally hundreds of rooms in the row of houses. Ma had the basement flat of number thirteen and we boys, George, Tim and me, were made to hide down there all day out of sight. Leading on from our basement were acres of disused cellars and if anyone came down to see Ma we retreated into the dark and stayed there, like cockroaches taking to the woodwork. We were totally happy.

We slept in the cellars too, on mattresses on the floor, and we always felt safe there even though the noise was often past bearing. We heard everything: the drone of the Junkers 88s, the high whine of the fighters, the banging of the anti-aircraft guns in the park and the explosions of the bombs, sometimes near, sometimes far away, round the railways, down by the docks. The most scarifying things were the whistling bombs. They dragged me upright on my mattress and made me listen to them come down, they held me rigid and motionless, sweating, sure and certain that the next one would get me, though I couldn't have been in a safer place, not in the whole of London.

Every day Ma made tea and sandwiches for the ladies who packed the parcels and cleaned their offices and swabbed down their stairs. Once the ladies had gone home we kids came out of hiding and continued our exploration of what we were coming to consider as our own private palace. We even had the good luck to find a little window at the back of the cellars which led directly to the park, giving us a way of escape if necessary. Ma was reassured by this discovery but she needn't have worried, we were three refugees the Red Cross never found.

Life was so much better suddenly than living alone in Arundel. I could roam as far as Berwick Market on one side and St James's Park and Whitehall on the other. Steve came to see us frequently, telling stories of work and the girls he knew. He was travelling now all over the country, camouflaging one airfield after another. His hands were paint-stained and he smelt different but he always gave us money, whether he could spare it or not. He was tall and he shaved too but his skin was clear and his face good-looking. His hair rose and fell in a smart quiff and he had brown eyes, like all of us, and they had long lashes which he could flicker like a girl if he wanted to make you laugh. He sang all the time. When he arrived at the weekends my mother's face would slip out from beneath its tiredness and she would chuckle just to see him. Steve did that to everybody.

Ma was well-liked too and the living-room at the bottom of the iron staircase was often crowded with people. Policemen, ARP wardens and ambulance drivers, the soldiers on guard duty round about, they would spend hours there, lounging in our armchairs, stretching their legs out in front of them, chatting, playing cards, brewing tea or making things for us boys. It was a regular home from home for half the neighbourhood. The men enjoyed talking to Ma and joking with her but she had the gift of putting them off with a laugh and they never got unpleasant. They gave her money to pay for the tea and sandwiches and the soldiers were always finding things to pass on. Tim gave up collecting coins and began on doorkeys instead.

There were other houses just as big on either side of us, but the connecting doors were locked at night and this restricted our exploring. But Tim's key collection grew into a series of huge bundles tied together with lengths of electric-light flex and soon there wasn't a door anywhere he couldn't open.

According to Ma Carlton House had once belonged to the Prince Regent and his servants had lived down in the cellars where we lived. The great ovens were still there and so were the lifts in the walls, once used for sending the food upstairs to the banquets. Often, even when connecting doors were locked, it was possible for us to bypass them by sailing upwards in a lift. The disadvantage of the lift-trick was that it was always me who did the sailing. I was the only one of us who was small enough to fit into a lift.

Occasionally some of the Red Cross ladies stayed late to get ahead with their packing, but it was something they hated doing because they had become convinced that number thirteen Carlton House Terrace was haunted by an energetic poltergeist. Their belongings changed places; doors, meant to be locked, were found swinging on their hinges; footsteps were heard; chairs faced the wrong way and waste-paper baskets were up-ended. It was terrifying.

Ma, who knew nothing about Tim's key collection, was just as puzzled about the ghosts as her employers were. Fortunately she was never suspected because she was always right there with them, working, and the packing rooms were double-locked every night.

It had all begun with the noises we used to make in the speaking-tubes that honeycombed the building. These tubes were shaped like old-fashioned telephones with a plug in the mouthpiece and we could force the most unearthly sounds down them. What we didn't realise was that the whistles and groans we made below could be heard all over the house, rooms and floors away from where we were. The ladies were certain their souls were in danger.

One evening George and Tim bundled me into a lift to search for chocolate in one of the packing rooms. I always hated the lift-trick. I was sure that one night the lift would get stuck and I would never get down again alive, that my body would be discovered weeks later, and Ma would lose her job.

The lifts worked on a rope and pulley system. I was pushed in by my brothers and they hauled away and up I went into the darkness, leaving the sound of their laughter further and further behind me. But as one lift rose another fell and the top lift of this particular pair was normally stationed in a corner of the packing room. The ladies of the Red Cross used it as a cupboard and that night it was stuffed with chocolate, boiled sweets, Horlicks tablets and cocoa. It was a treasure trove and worth a fortune on the black market.

As I arrived at the top of the shaft my two brothers saw an Aladdin's cave appear before their eyes. They stood stunned, they hadn't seen so many sweets since before the war. Meanwhile I, two floors up, was dying; I had jolted to a silent stop in the corner of a brightly lit room where the ladies were still working only a yard or two away from me, my mother dishing out tea in the middle of them. I sat there, crossed-legged, fearful, licking dry lips. I did not move once nor did I breathe for five minutes, the time it took my brothers to recover from their shock and to unload the lift down below. At last I felt the jerk on the ropes and I began to glide downwards. I was never more pleased at anything than to see that busy room float away upwards as I drifted down to the safety of the cellars.

I fell out of the lift and into a mound of sweets. George and Tim already had their cheeks bulging. I told them what had happened up above and we agreed never to do the lift-trick again because of Ma and her job, and we never did.

A few seconds after the upstairs lift had returned to its corner a woman reached round to take something from it and found it empty. As she'd only filled the lift a moment before, she shrieked, so Ma told us years later, and had to be led trembling from the room. Those Red Cross ladies were positive that number thirteen was haunted, and so it was, just as long as we three boys lived there.

The Blitz supplied me with a superb collection of shrapnel. I had regimental badges and buttons and shell-cases too, but shrapnel was my first love. It appeared overnight, like an alien growth. It took unnatural shapes, malignant colours, shades of green, mauve and blue. After every raid I was into the streets before the sound of the all-clear had died away and I found sprigs of shrapnel everywhere, sprouting along the gutters and glowing in St James's Park like exotic orchids of steel. Before long I had one of the finest collections in London. One night in 1940 I nearly collected a hundredweight of it in the brain.

By this time Gran had moved from the High Street to 34 Elspeth Road and we visited her whenever we could, generally about once a week. One Friday we slipped away from Carlton House Terrace and went down to Battersea for the whole evening. There were no sirens and not a plane could be heard in the sky, it was so quiet that we stayed at Gran's longer than we should have done. When we walked down the road to catch the tram home it was already dark.

The trams were wonderful in wartime. In all that uncertainty they were solid and reassuring, predestined to roll for ever along their silver rails, listing over like great red battleships. It was difficult to see out of a tram, their windows were covered with a criss-cross of adhesive material which was there to hold down the glass splinters when the bombs fell. Only one tiny rectangular gap was left clear by each seat, at eye level, so that passengers could squint into the blackout and try to guess where they were.

The seats were agony; narrow slats of yellow wood biting into the bum-bones, but the noises made by trams were infinitely superior to the ordinary drone of the ordinary bus. Trams lurched and groaned and creaked like frigates in a storm, they had spiral metal staircases set with polished studs, they had big brass driving handles and the driver could clang a bell by striking a knob in the floor with his foot.

It was the best way to travel and when you arrived at the end of the line there was no need to manœuvre a tram like you did with a bus. The driver simply walked from one end of the conveyance to the other and he found a new set of controls. The conductor pushed over the back of each seat and, in a minute, with a slap and a clatter, the interior of the tram was facing the other way. No machine in the world could compare with a tram.

George and Tim and Ma and me were the only people aboard that night and we went along brilliantly. Ma sang to us and we joined in with her as the old 26 churned along the tracks, the lights pale and solemn. Just before we got to Vauxhall they sounded the air-raid warning, the tram came to halt and the power went, the lights went and the driver and the conductress went. Ma, George, Tim and me were left sitting alone in a dark tram in the middle of the biggest raid of the war.

The ack-ack began first, far off towards the coast, then the explosions crept closer, vibrating the ground all around us. The searchlights came on and cut the sky into red quarters, ready for a game of noughts and crosses, and the bombers whined, keeping to the dark squares, mosquitoes after blood.

I don't think I would have been scared but Ma got scared and so we all did. She looked at us, worried, wondering how to get out of it, biting her lips till the teeth-marks showed white through the dark. She got us off the tram but there were no shelters and we didn't know which way to go. Ma needed to get back to Pall Mall in case of incendiaries on the roof, but there was so much of London burning that night that whether Carlton House Terrace burnt or not would have made very little difference. But she wanted to get us home, tucked safely into those deep cellars.

It was no good. The bangs and the blasts threw us this way and that. One minute we were feeling our way through a roaring darkness, the next our shadows were flashed silently onto huge walls that quivered in the moving air. Shrapnel pattered across the streets like wind-driven rain and every explosion was an end of life. By the time we got to Vauxhall railway bridge it seemed as if the whole Luftwaffe was aiming at us. George and Tim were swearing in fear. I was screaming. Ma was trying to carry me, but I was too heavy, her face was twisted and grey. We tried to take shelter by the bridge but the bombers were after every bit of track from Waterloo to Clapham Junction. My screams echoed along the walls and Ma, out of her mind, ran in circles, back-handing my brothers every other second.

It was the bottom of the war. We were going to lose and the Germans would get us first.

It was then that a tiny Cockney bloke turned up, like a dwarf from a drain. Lord knows where he came from.

'What's up, girl?' he said and Ma told him.

He was only a nobody from the Wandsworth Road but after he appeared everything went well. The raid was still as fierce as ever but he strutted along the pavement, shoulders straight, like he was taking us to the pub. He caught hold of me and told George and Tim to follow and he walked us through the middle of that raid, the two miles from Vauxhall to Pall Mall, whistling through his teeth. When we got home he wouldn't even come in for a cup of tea.

Ma ran, without stopping, up to the roof to see if it was on fire. It wasn't but the rest of London was. We followed her up and out into the open. It was like daylight up there away from the streets, only the light was red, bright red, a shepherd's delight of a sky. The raid was nearly over, the noise was receding back to the coast and the air was warm. Though there was nothing burning on our roof we could see silhouettes fighting flames nearby. St Paul's was ablaze and black smoke held the golden fires down over the City, reflecting the red glow sideways across the roofs and onto the skin of our faces and hands.

'My God,' Ma said, almost crying, 'there won't be anything left in the morning,' but there was.

Soon afterwards, about the middle of the war, after the Blitz but before the doodle-bugs, Steve was called up into the army and Ma became pregnant with my sister. There came a time when she couldn't hide it any more and she was sacked. The Old Man had found out where Ma had been hiding and he'd come round to

Pall Mall and they'd got together after months of separation. It wasn't long before they were quarrelling, like they always did, and he started hitting her again. I woke one night down there in the cellars and when I opened a door and looked into the light I saw him punch her. Ma got away from him and shouted for George to go for the police, even if she did lose her job. The Old Man hit George then, knocked him over, and left. His face was ugly and angry as he strode from the door, his body tall, dressed in the dark overcoat and Homburg hat.

We were all sad to leave Pall Mall; we liked living in the West End and we loathed the idea of going back to Battersea but there was no alternative. We moved from house to house to start with. The High Street again, then a flat halfway up St John's Road, by the railway bridge, till at last we settled into Lavender Sweep, a road on Lavender Hill by the Public Library. We took a flat in an old house on the left. It was so old, the neighbours said, that it had been built when there'd been nothing around it but endless slopes of lavender.

Every few yards along the road was a huge red-brick shelter bearing a concrete roof about a foot thick. When the air-raid warning sounded we had to jump out of our beds, pull the pillows and blankets down the stairs, and spend the rest of the night in a bunk in the shelter. Tim always refused to change beds like that, and so did Gran. 'If I'm going,' she used to say, 'I'm going to go warm, I ain't catching bronchitis for no Germans.'

Most people went early to the shelters. They arranged parties and dragged in crates of beer and sang late and loud when the raids got heavy, forgetting to go to work in the mornings. There was little ventilation in the shelters and the smell was thick and foul but there was no doubt that they saved thousands of us from the doodle-bugs and rockets.

Doodle-bugs were pilotless planes which, because they flew slowly, always gave some warning of their approach. They could even be shot down by our fighter-planes if they were spotted early enough on the radar. With the rockets, which came along later in the war, there was no hope because they travelled too rapidly to be seen. The first you knew of the rocket or V2 was the sound and shake of an explosion and half a street became a hole in the ground and the people who had lived there were particles of dust above your head and in your lungs.

I was left on my own many times in Lavender Sweep—Ma was a waitress again—and I saw scores of doodle-bugs. They carried just enough fuel to reach London and were packed with high explosive so that when they crashed to the ground they could cause an enormous amount of damage. They made a dirty noise as they flew, a continuous low farting sound. Flames burst from their rear end and when you caught sight of one you watched it carefully, because as long as you could see it you were safe; but your blood congealed in your veins the moment the motor cut out and it disappeared. Then you didn't know which way the bastard was going, it might be coming for you. On those days all you could do was run fast and bury your head. That long silent gliding, between the moment when the engine died and the shock of the explosion, was the longest silence in the world.

On the roof of my house once, when the warning siren went, instead of going straight to the shelter I stayed to watch. A doodle-bug came across the sky from down river, heading towards Wandsworth. It wasn't very high, near enough to touch, at two or three hundred feet. I could see the German crosses and swastikas easily. As I turned to run downstairs the noise stopped and that eternal silence began. I couldn't move. The whole of London seemed to stop as well and I could feel everyone in the world holding their breath and waiting for the bloody thing to glide down and I knew that everyone was thinking of those people who were going to die in a minute, sitting in their kitchens somewhere, drinking a cup of tea, not knowing what was coming to them, and I wished it wouldn't happen but knew at the same time it would.

I remember that bomb. It came down in Putney and killed more than forty people and I felt my bones move in the blast.

But they came nearer than that. At the bottom of the road, on the opposite side of the Hill, was a huge picture palace called the Pavilion. It had an enormous foyer with great columns in purple marble and it seemed like walking for ever before you got to the auditorium. The Pavilion, solid and luxurious, disappeared under a doodle-bug one day when I was indoors on my own about to spread a slice of bread.

Mrs Wilks, the lady from upstairs, came in almost as soon as the warning had gone.

'Come on, Mick,' she said, 'down the shelter.' I left my bread where it was, I hadn't put the jam on it, and ran down the stairs into the street.

We sat inside the shelter quite cheerfully waiting for the all-clear, and I was wishing I'd brought my bread and jam with me when we heard the doodle-bug arrive. It sounded near, driving down the street, insolent. We stopped talking and looked at each other and went pale. We all knew that those brick shelters couldn't stand up to a direct hit. I felt my stomach wrap itself around my backbone. The doodle-bug motor stopped and I heard the silence come and knock at the door.

'Down!' someone shouted and everyone got as close to the ground as they could. I got under a bunk. That was the trouble with those doodle-bugs, you had all the time in the world to be frightened. You knew that evil black thing was swooping across the sky, looking for you like a vulture after meat.

I lay there for a week, wanting to scream. Then the bang came. The bricks in the shelter rattled, the cement between them shook loose and the roof slab shifted. The door flew into the shelter, twisted and splintered. We got up, looked at each other and went out to find the street dark with a dust that smelt of burnt dirt and old flesh. Everywhere I walked I slipped on broken glass. I rushed upstairs to our flat and found that all the windows had gone, the wall between the living-room and the front bedroom was down and there was an inch of powdered plaster over my bread and jam.

I left it and went down to the bottom of the road where everyone else was going. At the top of the Hill, where the road dips down to the Junction and where the Pavilion had stood together with twenty or thirty shops, there was nothing but smoking rubble. The road was impassable, covered in debris as high as a hill. The string of shops on the left-hand side, opposite the cinema, had disappeared. Dust clogged my nostrils, making me cough and splutter. People were rolling wounded in the street, rolling in their own blood and groaning, cut by flying glass. I was told later that the doodle-bug had landed right on top of a 77a, everyone in the bus had been blown to smithereens and they'd found the conductress headless in a tree.

The police soon pushed us kids out of the way. Ambulances came and the Heavy Rescue started digging for the people who were buried under the wreckage. It was nasty when they dragged up the dead but it was worse when they began to find just bits of people and I turned faint and had to go home.

I walked up the street very slowly, my knees and arms were shaking. I heard machine-gun footsteps and Ma came running up behind me and grabbed me tightly and we cried into each other's shoulders. She had heard about the doodle-bug on the radio and without bothering to take off her white apron or her lace hat she had rushed out and taken a taxi all the way from Holborn to Battersea. She didn't know where the bomb had landed, on me or on Gran, but as Gran said when we went round there to see if she was still alive, 'If you hear the bang, mate, you can't be dead.'

When Ma saw the state of the flat she swore. It took hours to sweep up the dust and fix something at the windows. There was nothing we could do about the wall that had been blown down so we hung up a curtain and forgot it. I enjoyed that part; it seemed a practical short-cut from one room to another.

D-Day. We were going to attack the Germans in France and a feeling of excitement built up across the country. My exercise books were covered with caricatures of Adolf Hitler and drawings of burning German tanks. I destroyed countless Panzer divisions on my blue squares of blotting-paper.

In London Americans were everywhere, men in strange coloured uniforms with the voices of cowboys and pockets full of sweets. 'Got any gum, chum?'

Steve came to Battersea for his embarkation leave looking attractive and invincible in his khaki uniform. He hadn't been in the army long but he was convinced that tough times were ahead. We were just pleased to have him home for a few days, sad too. Steve was infantry and when we invaded Hitler there was every chance that he would stop a bullet. Even if he got through the landings the army still had to fight its way to Berlin, miles and miles. But Steve was determined to enjoy himself; he was cheerful, brimming with life. That weekend the flat was full of friends and family, the front door crashing open and shut day and night. Steve bought crates of beer and we laughed and joked and sang and drank. It was a long leisurely hysterical party, it went on for three days.

When he went Ma cried, sure she would never see him again.

Steve and thousands of other troops were being held in huge camps all along the south coast and after a while we discovered that he was at Ramsgate. We weren't supposed to know where he was, the troops wrote no addresses on their letters, but somehow we found out. Ma got some money together and decided to go and find him, feeling that it was her last chance before the invasion. She took me and my sister Evie with her.

When we arrived at Ramsgate we had nowhere to stay and had no idea what to do. A small section of the beach had been opened to the public, though the rest was still mined and covered in barbed wire. My sister had never seen the sea and she stared at it, not daring to touch it or go near it, frightened for her life, like when she first saw an orange when the war was over. To me paddling and thinking of all those Germans across a little bit of water, waiting to kill us, guns loaded, it was just creepy.

Ma settled down on the sand with Evie and she sent me out to look for Steve, not an easy job because there were thousands of troops in town. They were walking about in large groups, laughing and shouting. They stood on street corners and whistled at the girls and tried to make them stop and talk, but the girls put their chins on their shoulders, flashed their eyes and laughed amongst themselves, twitching their buttocks tight as they trotted on. The pubs, crammed with khaki, were loud and steamy with beery breath. I looked in all of them but couldn't tell one soldier from another. I knew that Steve was in the Hampshires and as soon as I saw shoulder-flashes I recognised I went up to the soldiers and asked them if they knew my brother. Some did, some didn't, but they agreed to spread the message and tell him that his family was waiting for him on the beach.

It worked. In less than an hour Steve came running to us, shouting and stumbling along in a spray of loose sand. He came with a dozen of his mates running behind him, big gawky soldiers with rough outdoor skins and red hands; they moved clumsily, their voices awkward, scarcely broken. Steve picked up my baby sister and threw her into the air and Ma leant back in her deck-chair and watched him, smiling, her eyes brilliant, brimming. She wore a hat, the sea wind flapped at the brim and she held it down with her hand, her brown hair blowing across her mouth now and then. Her face brightened and shone like a little girl's, she looked beautiful and happy. It was a wonderful afternoon and we sat and talked and looked at the sea, built sand-castles and played games—French Cricket, Hide and Seek, Cannon.

To me there was no game in the world so completely exciting as Cannon. All you needed to play it was a tennis-ball and four skinny bits of kindling wood about six inches long. You simply stuck three lengths of wood into the sand like cricket stumps, balancing the fourth piece across the top, and there was your 'cannon'.

In the streets, where we played the game most, we'd lean the sticks against a wall but that made no difference; Cannon was the same wherever you played it, marvellous.

The game was a struggle between two sides, equal in number to make it fair, and they were chance chosen by the 'dip' method. The 'dip' we used was a complicated one so that nobody could cheat and work out in advance where the finger would fall: 'Allah mallah mink monk, mink monk moozi, moozi moozi ah-bah, ah-bah boo. Boo boo chicka bong, Chinese junk, and O U T spells out'. . .

As soon as we were divided into teams we took it in turns to throw at the 'cannon' and the side that knocked it down scattered and ran; crouching, weaving, swerving. That team had to attack and keep on attacking and their task was to reconstruct the 'cannon'.

But their opponents set out to prevent them by means of the hard flung tennis-ball, a weapon that could kill on contact, for when an attacker was hit by it he was 'dead' and out of the game. The defenders guarded the 'cannon' fiercely, tossing the ball with care from man to man, waiting until they could pitch it at the enemy like a deadly harpoon, intent on annihilating them, one after another.

But the game could be won. The trick was to dodge and duck till the ball missed by a mile, bouncing beyond recovery for a moment, giving an attacker time to run in and re-erect the sticks, protected by a tight ring of valiant comrades.

The scoring of a 'cannon' was a great achievement and was always greeted with loud shouts and long yells by the victors. The losers had to suffer for a while, a few jeers, a few insults, but not for long. The dead were resuscitated, the 'all in' was called and the attackers

became the defenders and the defenders the attackers.
So it went on until finally the 'cannons' were totted up
and the side with the highest score was declared the
winner.

It was a rowdy game that day in Ramsgate. Most of
Steve's friends hadn't played before but they learnt in
no time and were soon running and skidding in the
sand, tumbling and falling over like children. Ma
wanted to watch only, but the soldiers pulled her out of
her chair and made her play with the rest of us. There
never was such a noise, or such a game. We shouted
and shrieked and the soldiers became so excited that
they ran into the sea, the water coming above their best
boots and gaiters and wetting their feet. More soldiers,
a huge crowd of them, and their girls stood above us on
the sea-front, looking down, watching and cheering our
two sides, clapping their hands and whistling. At the
end of it all, when we were exhausted, we went to a
cafeteria and had cream sodas and cakes. Evie and I
had anything we wanted that day, just as much as we
could get into our stomachs.

Steve quickly found us a place to sleep, good and
cheap. He hadn't been in Ramsgate long but he'd
organised himself a beautiful girl with black hair whose
mother owned a boarding-house and we spent the
whole week-end there. We saw Steve all the time and
his mates. We went to the pictures, sat in cafés, and
walked along the front eating fish and chips and buns.
And the beautiful girl came with us everywhere and
leant against Steve and put her head on his shoulder
and kissed him whenever she thought we weren't
looking. Everyone was so happy that it made me happy
just to look at them, to be part of them. People in the
street stopped to turn and look at this straggling,
irregular clump of happiness. Steve had his arms round

both his girl and Ma and he sang bits of song and
people smiled to see a soldier with two girls not letting
go of either of them. In the pubs Steve clutched both
women to him and said, 'They're both my girls, so
leave off ... and I've got another one at home.' He
meant Evie.

But we couldn't stay in Ramsgate for ever. All Steve's
mates came to the station to see us off, and so did the
beautiful girl and her thick hair swung round her face
as she looked first at Steve, then at Ma. Everyone got
platform tickets and made a laugh out of it, saying they
much preferred a day trip to London than a week in
France.

Steve's mates were embarrassed when he wanted to
say goodbye. They stepped to one side, fumbled with
their fingers and tried to see their faces in their bulled-
up boots. Their smiles went stiff on their mouths and
they turned away, some walking to the end of the
platform to face the wind, to be alone so we couldn't see
their tears as they wondered about their own mothers.

My Ma cried of course and just the sight of Ma
crying was enough to start Steve off. So I cried and
Evie cried and even the beautiful girl, who only loved
Steve, she cried. It was so funny to see us all crying
that it wasn't long before we were laughing.

'Come on, Ma,' Steve said, 'you'd better get on that
train ... you've got us all at it.' And he looked quickly
round at his mates to see if they'd seen him with tears
in his eyes, but they were far too busy walking up and
down with their own thoughts and their own tears. So
we got into the train and waved and the last drop of
happiness was squeezed dry out of us and the sadness
came down so strongly that I felt no other feeling could
alter it, ever. I was preserved in sadness, an eel, jellied.
The train dragged me away, willy-nilly, down the

platform, and I looked out of the window, hating the war for the first time, as Steve and the girl and the soldiers got smaller and smaller.

I kept my head outside for as long as I could see them. The wind blew my hair along the back of my head and over my ears. The wind slapped my eyes too and filled them with tears but what I saw remains unblurred: the green and cream paint of the station woodwork, sunlight shining on the concrete, and Steve's face as we pulled away, handsome, puzzled, full of concern, frightened of dying. And he had bright stiff boots with only a third of the sole touching the ground, the rest of it curling up sharply towards the toes. Above the boots were soft gaiters, blancoed, and above those were the keenest khaki creases in all the regiments of Ramsgate. And the beautiful girl clung to Steve, looking half-way happy because she had him to herself now, but looking sad too because she knew that soon, in a few weeks, it would be goodbye. Not like I'd said goodbye, with hardly a word intelligible, but with her arms around his neck and her eyes wet in his face and her voice saying, 'Goodbye, soldier, take care. You'll be all right, won't you Steve, you'll be all right, oh Steve, take care, don't go.'

Then the train was out of the station into bright sunlight, and the little khaki group had disappeared and we brought our heads in from the window, Ma and me, and I sat down to watch her cry.

Then we waited until it was D-Day. We listened to the nine o'clock news every evening and God help the kid who made a noise. It began badly. We landed and it went slowly, we got bogged down. Soon we started hearing about casualties and how the infantry had sustained heavy losses. Ma found it difficult to put up with the uncertainty. She became bad-tempered and I was careful not to step out of line.

When the letter came from the army it fell onto the lino like a paving-stone. Ma, Tim, Evie and me were indoors and Ma was crying before she opened the envelope and I couldn't stand it and ran into the bedroom and threw myself onto my bed. But I heard the crying change and Ma and Tim and even my sister Evie were shouting and jumping up and down and hitting the table with their hands and throwing plates on the floor. They ran into my room then, all three, and jumped on the bed, pulling the clothes off it and rolling me up in them. Steve was alive!

He'd been going up the gangplank, ready to board the boat that was to take him over the Channel, when he'd collapsed with a temperature of a hundred and something. He'd caught dysentery in the camp but he'd told no one because he hadn't wanted to be separated from his unit. But the officers, watching the men closely as they went into the landing craft, had noticed that Steve looked ill and they had ordered him back. They'd had to drag him ashore and he'd been kept in hospital for three weeks.

When Steve came home he looked washed out, altered. He was quiet, thinner, the old spark had gone.

'Do cheer up,' Ma kept saying, 'you're alive and back here with us, unharmed, in one piece.'

But nothing could lift Steve out of his depression. He took down all the photos we had taken that day in Ramsgate.

'I ain't got the right to show those photos, Ma,' he said, 'no right to be in them. They're all dead, Ma, all of them, except me, and I should be by rights.'

But as far as Ma was concerned she could have asked for nothing better. It was beginning to look like we'd get through the whole war without a scratch. We'd had narrow escapes in the bombings but we were still all together. Steve was out of the landings and it was some time before he was sent to another unit. He went all the way through to Germany eventually but as a driver and never in the front line. Even so the war showed him some horrible things: towns totally destroyed with people starving and dying in the ruins, concentration camps stinking with piles of rotting bodies, women selling themselves to get a square meal for their kids, their husbands dead.

But for us it was over. We were safe; apart from a rocket on Prince's Head which blew up St Mary's and a few hundred people out shopping, World War Two in Battersea was finished.

EDUCATION'S
A MARVELLOUS
THING

But there was another war going on in Battersea in 1944, the hostilities between Wix's Lane and Tennyson Street. I was ten years old and the school I went to was up an alley, Wix's Lane, three tram stops away from Lavender Sweep. The other kids in my street went to Honeywell Road but Ma thought Wix's Lane was better. It was pretty rough, but not as rough as Tennyson Street.

There were no kitchens at Wix's Lane and every dinner-time the whole school, about four hundred of us, had to walk about a mile to Tennyson Street. It was one long fight there and back, across a desert landscape of bombed sites and holes in the ground where kids were always throwing stones and bricks at one another. The Tennyson Street kids thought they were much tougher than we were and attacked us almost every day. We took to travelling in large groups but it didn't solve much, the fights just became bigger. Luckily for me my cousin Joe was in the top class at my school and he was tall and strong. On the way to Tennyson Street I followed Joe and his friends for protection. When the fights started I ran with them and I fought with them.

Generally I tried to stay out of trouble, but it didn't matter how crafty I was, sooner or later there'd be a fight and Woodsie, our headmaster, would sniff us out and we'd get a beating, a good one. Woodsie frightened everybody, the small boys, the big boys, his own

teachers. Some people said he was mad and he certainly
looked it. I couldn't speak when I stood in front of him;
black hair, red face and a hundred miles tall. He never
went anywhere in the school without a bundle of
twenty canes under his arms, all sizes, all shapes—fat
heavy ones, middling ones and thin little wispy ones
that could take the skin off your hand and bring out
the blood. You only had to cough, sneeze or fart in his
presence and you were in for it. He stood up above you
selecting a stick from his bundle, taking his time,
making you wait. By the time he got round to the
actual beating your mind had drained away and you
were jabbering with fear.

Every morning at Assembly we sang hymns and
chanted prayers, then we trembled while the monster
prowled amongst us searching for victims. Woodsie
did all the work and enjoyed it, selecting the right cane
for the job, lecturing while he did so, telling us about
each 'malefactor'. It took courage not to cry when you
were beaten because Woodsie hit you as hard as he
could, jumping a foot into the air to bring the stick
down, and breathing out so loudly that you could hear
him panting as far away as the back row.

You got the stick for everything at Wix's Lane:
being late, playing truant, getting in Woodsie's way,
running in the corridors, dropping milk-bottles out the
windows, slamming doors, not paying your fares on the
trams, but above all you got it for fighting with
Tennyson Street.

Nobody who had any sense wanted to fight with
Tennyson Street, but fights there were. It was no good
saying it wasn't your fault or you hadn't started it. If
you were reported you were beaten. The real war had
been fun most of the time, an adventure; the war with
Tennyson Street was simply ugly. That mile walk at

midday became a hideous trek into danger and back
again. The roads were long and littered with glass and
stones. The walls were high and unfriendly, the open
spaces windy and cold. It was a no-man's land full of
enemy snipers. Many kids I knew went without their
dinners rather than walk to Tennyson Street, I was
very often one of them. But in spite of my being as
cunning as I could I became involved in the biggest
battle of them all.

There were only a few of us to start with.

I was walking with Joe and half a dozen of his
friends, tough lads they were. Joe himself was fourteen
and due to leave school about then. We were taking a
short cut across a rugged bombed-site where the hard-
packed dirt rose and fell over demolished walls and
half-hidden cellars; it was the middle of nowhere.
Suddenly a horde of Tennyson Street thugs came out
of the ground like savages. We were surrounded,
trapped.

There seemed to be hundreds of them. They charged
up out of the craters, they leant from the windows, they
were even up on the roofs. They jeered at us, throwing
everything they could lay their hands on, bricks, tiles,
and bits of glass. I was scared. I think Joe was scared.
We were out-numbered and we didn't stand a chance.

We retreated into the ruins of a bombed yard and
broke down a wall to use as ammunition. We fought
hand to hand too and cleared ourselves a refuge on the
ground floor of a derelict house and there we were safe
for a while. At one point the Tennyson boys gathered
in a crowd to make a charge, but we had collected a
complete arsenal of missiles and before they could
attack we did. It was wonderful to see them turn and
run. I flung a brick in a high swinging arc, flung it
with all my strength and watched it curve like fate to

crash onto the heel of an enemy who writhed away in pain down a loose slope of rubble. We raised a cheer and fought harder.

A moment later everything went quiet. It was the kind of quiet that comes into a playground when a policeman walks through it. It was Woodsie and the headmaster from Tennyson Street; someone had telephoned them.

We stood there trying to look as if we were somewhere else and without bricks in our hands. It was the only time I ever saw Woodsie without the bundle of canes under his arm, but I knew that he wouldn't be long without them. Woodsie lined us up and looked pleased. He smiled like a hacksaw at Joe, he didn't like my cousin. He wrote our names down and he smiled at me too. Then he went back to Joe.

'You're leaving soon, aren't you, Leary?' Joe nodded. 'I'll have to give you something to remember me by.' He sent us back to Wix's and we waited outside his office; we knew what to expect. Some of the teachers saw us there and asked what had happened. They wanted to take us away and wash our cuts because we had been so badly knocked about, but nobody dared to do a thing without Woodsie's permission.

Looking back I can never understand why we didn't refuse to be caned. Why did we put up with it? We could have revolted, gone on strike, or simply not gone back to school after the fight. We must have been as stupid as we were scared.

Woodsie picked out his swishiest canes for us that day and he still managed to break a few. Joe did his best to get me off but it didn't work.

'He's only ten, sir . . . it wasn't his fault . . . he was just walking along with us and once it had started . . . sir.'

Woodsie just grinned like someone who'd won all

your cigarette cards and said mysterious and unanswerable things about the cranes and the stork.

The lads got two on each hand and two on the arse; with that swishy cane it hurt like hell and the pain lasted for several days. Even the big fellows cried, some of them struggled and all of them swore. Joe stepped up and took his as it came. Woodsie hit him with every ounce of bone and muscle he had. Afterwards Joe looked at Woodsie and he wasn't scared of him one bit any more. He spoke up, man to man. 'I'll get you, Woodsie, when I'm out of this dump; you beat my cousin and I'll slice you to bits, me and the others.'

But Woodsie wasn't scared either and he did beat me though he only gave me four, one on each hand and two on the behind. I cried, but not much, not with Joe there.

In a way it was worth it afterwards when the worst of the pain had worn off. The rest of the kids in the school couldn't wait to hear what had happened. Four hundred of them crowded round us in the playground. We even had to slide our trousers down a bit so they could see the red weals on our buttocks. Joe had a big bruise on the side of his head and a black eye and all of us were scarred from the battle. The kids in my class couldn't get over me being in a fight and a caning with the lads from the top of the school, I was a hero. If Woodsie looked down from his office on the fourth floor that day he must have seen how popular we were, surrounded by a mob of jostling and elated children.

Joe had always been a celebrity but his reputation was assured by what he had said to Woodsie. He was much envied at Wix's, mainly because he looked about sixteen or seventeen and, most wonderful of all, he went out with girls who'd already left school and didn't mind telling you what he'd done with them on the

Common. Joe's contemporaries admired and disbelieved him all at once.

'It's easy to say you've done it, Leary, anyone can say anything.'

Joe laughed, he could prove it, nothing easier. He wouldn't mind even if they all watched, just as long as everyone paid five shillings for the privilege. He must have made a couple of quid out of it because more than a dozen of us went and he told me afterwards that he only gave the girl ten bob. I went for nothing, being family, though some of the lads tried to stop me, saying that I was too young, but Joe had his way. Without him there would have been nothing to see.

We met on the Common by the football pitches because it was the only bit with trees and bushes, where you could hide. We could hear the shouts of the footballers playing on the cinders and the noise of the traffic coming home from work. Joe came up with the girl and we stood about in a group, kicking the grass. The girl was all right, about sixteen, with a tight blouse stretching open between the buttons. She wore a little black skirt, tiny shoes, scuffed at the toes, and she had a spotty chin which she kept touching with her bitten-down fingernails.

We waited for about half an hour. I got so bored that I nearly went home. I don't think the girl minded doing it but there were far too many of us watching. At last Joe ordered us to move away behind some bushes and he told me to keep an eye open for the keepers. I climbed into a tree so that I could see right across the Common.

Once the girl began she wasted no time. She lay on her back and let Joe do whatever he wanted. I think what surprised me most was the matter-of-fact way it all happened, I hadn't imagined it like that. Joe pushed up her skirt and pulled her knickers off so that both her legs were free. I saw the black gash between her legs and was frightened by it. He undid the girl's blouse and I saw her nipples. He began to pummel her breasts with his hands, getting up on his knees to manage both at once. The girl stared into the tree, studying my face dispassionately, as if it had been nothing but a curious fruit hanging above her. After a moment Joe unbuttoned his trousers and covered her body with his own.

His arse looked small and pink. He must have got inside her then because her knees came up and Joe's behind moved up and down, quicker and quicker. She put her arms round his neck and her legs went higher, her feet left the ground.

It was the first time I'd seen it and I saw it all, they were right underneath me. I was disappointed, I'd expected more. It was over in a couple of minutes. I looked up. Joe's mates protruded from the green leaves where they'd half-hidden themselves to watch. I could see every one of them, scattered round the clearing, their white faces silly and shocked, balanced on the bushes like pale artificial flowers, bloodless and without expression. They looked at each other puzzled. Was that it? Was that all? People made all that fuss over this?

Joe sat up, tidied the front of his trousers, and handed the girl her drawers. The boys pushed out from the undergrowth and I climbed down from the tree. We looked at the girl with a kind of respect; she knew it all, more than we would ever know. I wouldn't have been surprised if we'd said 'Thank you very much' to her, but we didn't.

Joe looked red-faced and stupid but the girl looked no different. She stepped into her knickers, yanked them up to her crutch, wriggled her bum comfortable, pulled at her skirt and smoked one of our cigarettes. As soon as she'd finished it she left, saying she had to start off home at once otherwise her mother would wallop her for being late for tea. She walked quickly away across the Common on her own, a tiny figure taking short steps, running every now and then in short bursts.

Joe left school a little later. He could have stayed on at Wix's for the extra year but he didn't think it was worth it. His first job was as a trainee waiter in Lyons and he stayed in the work for years. When Uncle Ned, his father, came home from a prisoner-of-war camp, he told Joe he'd done the right thing.

'Those buggers at school can't teach you any more, son,' he said, 'if they taught you anything at all. I tell you that headmaster was lucky I wasn't here when he thrashed you. I'd have dragged him out in front of the whole school and beaten the life out of him. I'da done prison for him too if needs be, a bloody pleasure.'

Uncle Ned's words made the rest of my time at Wix's easy to bear. Whenever I saw Woodsie I was warmed by a secret thought. Ned was back now, I had only to give him the sign and he would storm down to the school, strip Woodsie in front of us all, and beat him with every one of the twenty canes, shaming him, making him cry like he'd made us kids cry. Woodsie was in my power.

'Education's a marvellous thing,' Uncle Ned used to say to me with a laugh on his face. 'Every politician you've ever heard of was educated up to the eyeballs at this or that public school and look what a mess they've made of the world, just look at it. Two wars in twenty years, the bastards, and we do the fighting. This was the war to end all war, was it? Bollocks! Like saying that it was the hangover to end all hangovers! Don't you worry, son, they'll soon have a war going for you lot, don't worry your head about that. Nothing changes, nothing. The only thing we've got rid of is the red coats, the rest is the same. Keep out of it, Mick, use your bloody loaf. As for beating little kids when our backs are turned, scaring the life out of them, that's education, is it? Well, I've seen enough of that to last me a lifetime. Teachers—more like prison guards! I tell you, Mick, get out of school as quick as you can, live by your lights, be good to your own and above all look after number one because that's what they do; it's the only way the likes of us stands a chance in this world.'

Ned hadn't had an easy war. He'd been five years a prisoner and every minute of it had been a struggle.

'Five lost years,' he'd say and he'd swear. 'No way of getting them back either.'

I hardly recognised Ned when he came home. I'd been five years old when I'd last seen him at Arundel with uncle Dennis. I was eleven when he was repatriated.

He had been taken prisoner at Dunkirk together with thousands of others who'd been holding the perimeter so that the British Expeditionary Force could get back across the Channel. The Germans had been overjoyed to capture a large number of British troops and had frog-marched them through Belgium and France in order to demonstrate how powerful the German Army was. When the prisoners were exhausted they'd been herded into iron goods trucks, stuffed in so tightly with rifle butts and bayonets that there was hardly room for a man to breathe and none at all for him to fall over.

It was sweltering hot and the sun beat down day after day onto the curved metal roofs. They were a fortnight on the journey, hardly fed or watered and never let out. The smell of the filth and the dead and the dying was a stench from hell. By the time they got to Poland only five men crawled out of Ned's truck alive.

'There were plenty of men standing up,' Ned said, 'only they were dead, they had been for days.'

He spent the war digging roads, loading and unloading anything that needed loading or unloading. He worked down mines, on farms and in factories. He was a slave.

'Working for wages is bad enough,' Ned reckoned, 'but working for those bastards, against yer own kind, that's murder.' All he could do was keep his head down, keep going and survive.

The Russian prisoners had it far worse. They were beaten regularly and taken out in batches to the woods and shot against the trees after they'd dug their own graves. They were lucky to see any food at all and many died from starvation or from being too weak to resist disease.

Ned tried to help. Whenever he went by the Russian camp with a cart-load of turnips he always threw over as many as he could. Occasionally the British prisoners worked side by side with the Russians. Ned made friends with a man from Leningrad and whatever they had they shared.

'It was amazing,' Ned explained, 'the talent we developed for knocking off stuff to eat, even when there was nothing there, nothing for miles.'

When the Red Army began advancing across Poland and the Germans realised the game was up they gathered all their prisoners together and began a forced march that was to last months and leave thousands dying by the roadside.

'Blokes were dropping like flies,' Ned told us, 'lying like bundles of rags in the ditches. The Germans shoved bayonets into them as they passed...don't know why, they'd have died of the cold in two minutes.

Our only chance of staying alive was to scrabble in the fields for rotten potatoes and to set snares for cats and dogs. But it didn't matter how many prisoners died the Germans kept going. Dead scared of the Russians, weren't they?'

All this time the Russian and the British prisoners were kept separate, the Germans believing that if the two groups got together they might become unmanageable. Because of this Ned never expected to see his mate from Leningrad again. But he was wrong.

One night, about a month after they'd set out, Ned's mob of prisoners was locked into an old barn with just a few German soldiers on guard outside. In the middle of the night Ned woke to hear a strange voice whispering in his ear, 'Ned . . . Ned . . . komm with us,' and he opened his eyes to see his Russian friend kneeling over him.

He'd come all the way across the town to find Ned, completely fooling two sets of armed guards to do it. There was a great commotion going on outside where three more Russians were creating a din to confuse the German sentries. Ned and the man from Leningrad went through the cordon of guards easily enough and crept across the nameless town which lay desolate about them. When they got to the Russian camp the diversionary tactics were repeated and soon they were safe inside another barn.

It was unbelievable: a great feast had been prepared.

At some time during the day the Russian column had marched across a farm. They'd gone in empty-handed and come out with a pig, slaughtered on the spot, cut into sections and concealed under their greatcoats. The German guards hadn't even noticed a pig. As soon as the prisoners had been bedded down for the night the cooking began and the man from Leningrad had decided to fetch Ned for the banquet.

81

It lasted well into the early hours and never had pork tasted so good. When Ned left to return to his barn he carried enough meat to keep him going for days, as well as bones to suck. He was again escorted by some of the Russian prisoners and they saw him back to safety. Ned was convinced they were carrying guns already because they seemed scared of no one, least of all the German patrols. Ned never met the man from Leningrad after that, but he has never forgotten him and he won't hear a word against Russians. 'They're good men, good fighters and good friends,' he said.

The marching went on week after week. Finally there was hardly any room left between the American front and the Russian front and nowhere for the Germans to go. They stopped as near to the American lines as they dared and sat down to think things out. The prisoners were held in some huge sandpits and they lay motionless, exhausted, hungry, waiting.

An American spotter plane saw them all and dropped leaflets ordering the Germans to hand over their prisoners unharmed. It was that or surrender to the Red Army, which was just what the guards had walked several hundred miles to avoid.

Under a white flag the Germans and their captives walked towards the Americans with the plane overhead. When they arrived at the Allied positions the prisoners suddenly realised that they were free and jumped on the guards and began to tear them limb from limb with their bare hands, enjoying it.

'The Americans could only stop us by firing over our heads,' Ned told us. 'They threatened to shoot us for real if we didn't. They had to beat us back with rifle butts; they'd had it too easy, didn't know what we'd been through. The Russians weren't so silly, we heard what they did. Just before they got to the American lines they jumped their guards and skewered them up a bit on their own bayonets, cut their bollocks off, then slit their throats and sat down to watch them bleed to death. When they'd finished they strolled in on their own, cool as cucumbers, and asked for cigarettes. That's what we should have done. The only good German's a dead one, and if you meet a good one, kill him before he turns bad.'

Ned took his shirt off when he'd finished his story and showed us his back; it was covered with scars.

PEACE
IS DECLARED

Steve danced up the street in his demob suit and everyone leant from the windows and laughed at his baggy striped trousers and at the way he shoved the shoulder pads of his jacket halfway down his back. The brim of the brown trilby he pushed upwards above his face and when he got in front of the house he put down his cardboard case, took a running kick at it and then skimmed his hat over the roof. We'd moved to the street while he'd been away and none of the neighbours knew him much, but they soon did.

It didn't take him long to spend his demob money. He bought my mother and sister some clothes and me a second-hand bike so that I could cycle to school and save the tram fare. What was left of his money went across the saloon bar at the Falcon. Ma was always telling Steve that he was his own worst enemy, spending good money on a troop of spongers, but he would just let his old smile break through and Ma would have to smile as well. 'He could charm Nelson down to Charing Cross,' was what they said of Steve.

London had been a village during the war and every Londoner had been a villager. We'd talked to strangers, joked about the rationing and helped one another when we could. Everyone was on the fiddle but that was accepted and we shared what we had. We'd sung songs in the shelters and the Americans had been wonderful, the Russians too. It had all been so simple;

we'd had one enemy and he had been common to us all. We had hated the Germans straightforwardly and energetically. If they won the war there was no future, no life, no freedom. If things went wrong from day to day, well, it was the war's fault. 'Post-war', as we called it, would be the millennium.

The millennium, when it came, was a disappointment. Everything changed for the worse and there was no excitement to compensate. The war was over and the world went quiet. The danger that had wrapped us all together in one warm lump had gone. What would happen now? What could happen now? Was there anything to live by at all when there was no enemy? The world began to look different. It curdled and fell away into its separate parts, like a bottle of milk left too long on the doorstep. Everything was to begin again, everything had to be rediscovered.

We gave a party for Steve after the war. Ours was a large flat with three bedrooms, but it was cold most of the time and we tended to crowd together in the living-room and the kitchen. The geyser in the bathroom never worked properly so we took it in turns to have thorough washes at Gran's in Elspeth Road.

On the night of the party hundreds crowded into the flat. The living-room and hall were full of neighbours and cousins and young couples were leaning against each other on the landing and down the stairs which led to the street. My uncles were there of course, my aunties too and their husbands, every one of them a spiv according to my mother. The party was a noisy one and went on into the night with Auntie Molly, Jane and Kath dancing with my brothers and their own sons too. They all got tipsy and squeezed each other's shoulders and cried because the war was over and done with. Uncle John drank too much whisky and insulted us all, doing his best to provoke a fight, but he always did that and we knew what to expect from him. At last he was shoved out onto the pavement to fight with himself.

'He's been fighting with himself all his life,' said Auntie Molly. 'If you'd been married to him for years like I have you'd know what I've had to put up with. Trouble with John is that he can't stand people happier than he is, and as most of them are he's had a miserable life.'

My mother was quiet at these family celebrations. She looked after everybody, but once the party was going she liked to sit in a corner, chuckling to herself quietly, watching her boys sing or dance and play the fool. She wasn't a great one for showing physical affection but at some time during the party she rubbed my hair with her hard hand and I heard her say to Jane, 'I hate seeing my kids grow up, don't you? They don't know what's waiting for 'em, do they?'

I never forgot her saying that; it was another mental jump for me, like uncle Ned's sunlit shirt-cuffs. I realised, that evening just after the war, that my Ma was in fact a separate person, with her own thoughts and worries, separate from me and my wants. I suddenly saw that she'd once been a young girl and I tried to imagine what her childhood had been like, to visualise how she had grown up into the world to be alone, just like we all did.

The weekends were the best time in Lavender Sweep, except Saturdays when I was sent right across London on a 77 bus to see the Old Man in his flat in Russell Square. I suppose Ma sent me because I was the only person she could force to endure such a dreary morning and because I was supposed to be my father's favourite, a distinction I bore with an ill will.

My job was to wheedle money out of him, as much as I could. I came to hate that weekly trip and I came to hate the Old Man because of it. Over a long period of years I had every Saturday morning, and some Saturday afternoons, stolen from me and thrown away.

The Old Man couldn't bully Ma completely because she was too tough and independent, but he got at her through our need for money. He did anything to keep her short, so at last she gave up asking him for cash and took to sending me instead. Perhaps he never noticed who I was but he certainly made me pay a thousand times over for every quid and I never forgave him for it. I was a small boy burning with hatred, a land-mine ticking at his heels.

He lived in a big block of service flats, a totally different world to the one I was used to. His way of life was different, his friends were different and they talked in a way that was hard to understand, articulate and supercilious. They were well-mannered and to me therefore untrustworthy. Their nails were polished, their overcoats immaculate. My father's difference robbed me of all ambition. If that was success I didn't want it. I didn't want clean nails and dark suits if it meant being like him and his friends; I'd stay where I was.

It was torture to be with him. He would introduce me to his friends and I'd try not to speak. I spoke in pure Cockney and they always looked at me, surprised, and the Old Man would explain my accent by blaming it on my mother. That made me furious and angry but I said nothing. My father frightened me to death, tall and big-faced, serious, hardly laughing except to mock something I'd said. I was dirty too, and he'd scrub my nails and sometimes bath me and that was the worst. I hated his touch.

As soon as I was clean enough, subdued enough, we went, in a taxi, to Fleet Street where the Old Man did most of his work as a press agent or freelance journalist and photographer. At least he said he was all those things, but whatever he did he managed to scrape a living together without working for anyone directly.

On lucky Saturdays he took me into the bank, drew out a few pounds, handed over a couple and sent me home on the next bus. The suitcase I had brought empty from Battersea would be placed in my hands, magically grown heavy, filled with butter and meat, while he'd been in a bar or on the back staircase of some newspaper office. On unlucky Saturdays I had to follow him from pub to pub, from the Mitre to the Cheese, from the Wig and Pen to El Vino's, while he tracked down a debt or made long attempts to raise a loan.

Sometimes I got to his flat too early and he wouldn't let me in. After a while he'd come into the corridor, his dressing-gown smelling of cigars, perfume and whisky, press a shilling into my hand and tell me to visit the British Museum for an hour. I didn't mind going to the museum, in fact I enjoyed it. It was there I learnt all about the Rosetta Stone and Napoleon. I wrote an essay about it just before I left Wix's Lane and the teacher nearly came out in spots when she read it. No, I didn't mind the Old Man sending me off, but it used to annoy me that he took me for an idiot, fobbing me off with lies when I knew he had a woman in there. I used to hide and watch her come out sometimes and it wasn't always the same one.

But eventually I would get away from Fleet Street and clamber high up to the top of a bus, the suitcase with me, feeling piously content. I'd got a few quid for Ma, as well as a suitcase full of rationed grub, so she'd be pleased. I also had a few warm coins for myself, handed down to me by the Old Man's damp-handed acquaintances, and I had the afternoon in front of me too. I could gaze from the bus and watch the West End disappear. Soon I'd cross the Thames at Lambeth Bridge, and once beyond Vauxhall I was nearly home, in streets I knew, where people talked straight.

In the afternoon my brothers and uncles came back from the pub loaded with bottles and sat around talking the hours away while my Ma tried to dry the washing on the fire-guard and iron shirts for the weekly dance at Battersea Town Hall. Evie crawled about the floor, inspecting everyone's shoes and crying when she was trodden on. The living-room smelt of steam, cigarette smoke, beer and the mouldy dustbin that lived secretly in a cupboard behind the kitchen. Everyone talked, everyone laughed. When I got back with the Old Man's money Ma would send me out to do the weekend shopping. I didn't mind that too much because I was expert at wriggling to the front of queues, getting more than the correct amount of change, and stealing the extra packet of grub here and there, especially the rationed stuff. What was more, anything I made over the top was mine. But what I really loved, as soon as those Saturday jobs were over, was to crawl under the table in the living-room and listen to the men talking.

Once Steve's army gratuity had gone he took a local job at Morgan's Crucible Works, by the Battersea Bridge. He couldn't hold it down for long. 'He's too restless now,' my Ma said, 'he needs something that gets him out and about, like during the war.' Steve's next job was with a demolition firm, travelling across the country to knock down shelters and aerodromes. A little later he became a long-distance lorry-driver, which was work he liked because he went everywhere, he was his own boss and there was no one to tell him when he could or couldn't stop on the road to have a quiet pee and a smoke, looking at the sky.

'Plenty of crumpet, too, on the road,' he said, 'working their passages from Land's End to John o' Groats,' and he'd wink and recount the week's adventures.

He could make us laugh so easily, tears ran down our faces and Ma would spit on the iron and shake her head. The key was always in the lock of the front door and the whole world was in and out; uncles, aunties, cousins and neighbours borrowing a quid for the pub or the dogs.

On Sundays all the men gathered on the landing before going down the Hill in a big group to drink at the Falcon. I would follow them, sent to buy the Sunday papers from the man at the Junction, and I always waited there until someone bought me a lemonade to drink, standing outside on the windy pavement. I used to stare at the pub doors and when they sprang backwards and forwards on their each-way hinges short whiffs of hops and damp sawdust were fanned out to me and I would catch alternating glimpses of a crowded bar ... Steve, George, Tim, Harry, John, Ned, Frank, and even Uncle Dennis who'd come back alive after four years in the siege of Malta. They moved carefully in circles, around each other, not spilling their drinks, or they leant against the wooden counter in a mob, laughing, their faces shiny and flushed with beer, throwing their heads back and swallowing the golden Bass in huge bitter mouthfuls.

A year or so after the war the Falcon acquired a new and flashy barmaid and the men were soon sniffing at

93

her like randy dogs. She wore lots of make-up and gold jewellery, her bangles made tinny noises when she worked the pumps. She had red hair, very dark in the waves, and her eyes were pale, pale green. They said she came from Bristol but no one ever knew. Her voice was low and lazy and it laughed at you. Her bones were big and they were wrapped in an eiderdown of flesh. Her skin was a frightening white.

When she walked her thighs ground the dark parts of her stockings one against the other and the abrasive silk swish set a man's teeth on edge and hurt his groin. She moved her arms and the lovely breasts dragged her blouse tight and drew the eye. She was powerful, brimming with sex, even I could see that. She looked at a man like a policeman looks at a dud fiver, superior, haughty, but still thinking that one day it might come in useful.

Her large mouth was moist and mobile under crimson lipstick, but behind the smear of pleasantness it was truculent and hard. The smiles could not hide the contempt. Her name was June, she'd been everywhere, seen everything, knew everyone.

'And she's had everybody too,' my mother said. 'Thinks with her fanny she does, all tits and bangles.'

Because of June's habit of saying, 'D'you know what I know?' or 'D'you know this?' or 'D'you know that?', people didn't call her June at all, but Juno. Whenever she started a conversation the men at the bar would laugh and introduce their friends and say, 'That's Juno, you know . . . you know Juno.'

The men at the Falcon adored the woman. Every time you saw her she had hold of a different man. One weekend when Steve came home they told him about her, laughing, in our living-room, with me under the table listening. Steve chuckled and he dressed himself

up like a pox-doctor's clerk and went down to the
Falcon to look at her. When he walked into the pub he
nearly fell off his feet, laughing. He already knew Juno,
from the time he'd been in the army. She'd been a
NAAFI girl with a reputation that had covered more
than one barracks and Steve had stolen her from the
other soldiers and lived with her for a month or two.
He stole her again from the men at the Falcon and he
did them a bloody good turn. It was the worst day's
work he ever did in his life.

Six months later Steve and Juno disappeared for a
day. When they came back they were very secretive
and laughed, saying they'd got married quietly but no
one in the family believed a word of it. It didn't make
any difference, they were as good as married even if
they weren't. It was 1947.

It was the end too. We all knew it was a mistake,
perhaps Steve did, but he didn't seem to care. 'All be
the same in a hundred years,' he'd say when you
criticised him. Nobody could work up any enthusiasm
for Juno however hard they tried and everyone attempted to talk Steve out of it. Uncle Ned argued with
him one whole night, eventually storming off in a
temper and I heard him shouting as he went down the
stairs. 'You're cunt-struck, Steve, cunt-struck, that's
your trouble.' But Steve just laughed and gently shut
the front door, saying, 'What's it matter? All be the
same in a hundred years.' But it did matter and I began
to look at Steve and worry about him, and I suppose
Ma did too.

Juno waited on Steve hand and foot at first but it
didn't last long.

'If she isn't pregnant already,' Ma said, 'then you
mark my words, she'll get up the spout as soon as she
can.' She was right. Within a few months Juno had had

a baby boy and was into the happy mother stage: big prams with big wheels, fawn sunshades with long fringes. She pushed her chrome pram along the Falcon Road and around Prince's Head and told everybody she met what a wonderful mother she was.

'Wait until she's had thirteen of the bleeders,' said Gran, 'then we'll see how Upcomely-Bleedin'-Bagshot she is about that.'

Most afternoons the pram was parked outside some pub or other. We told Steve but he was too proud to hear. He thought that if he kept the money coming in Juno would be happy and it would all sort itself out.

It didn't. Juno had another boy and then a girl after that. She couldn't handle so many, it wasn't worth her trying and she didn't. She went to bed and decided to stay there until the children grew up. During the day, every day, her kids crawled over each other like pale crabs, fighting in their own shit and surviving off fistfuls of cornflakes.

Juno and Steve lived in Rowena Cresent, at the other end of Battersea from us. My mother used to go straight to their flat after her waitressing to clean up and cook the children a meal. She wasn't able to take the extra strain for long, two or three years of it soon tired her out. George had married and left home by this time and Tim had got a job away, but Evie and I were at school. Juno's kids, the washing, the cooking, the working, it was all too much for Ma; you could see the strength begin to drain from her. I think it was the shame of it more than anything, seeing her grandchildren neglected, running wild, half-dressed no matter how cold it was, their nostrils flowering with green snot, a chunk of grubby bread folded into their hands. Soon my mother could stand it no longer and stopped going to Steve's flat, looking the other way if she saw the ragged band of kids in the street, and she began to look older, from one day to the next.

Soon the tremendous rows began and Steve took to hitting Juno, hard. She ran into the streets then, screaming, staying away for days, hanging around the pubs, sleeping anywhere, and Aunt Jane and my mother were left with the children until Juno returned, her legs weak, her green eyes deep in her head.

Steve still believed that money could save the marriage and the children. He worked harder for a while and drove further and stayed away from Juno as much as he could. He bought things in great eruptions and splashes of cash, throwing his kids' clothes away because they were dirty and rigging them out afresh. For twenty-four hours his kids would look fine, then it was back to normal.

Eventually he gave up trying, even that last little bit. He stayed on the move. He'd always liked a good time and now he spent every free moment he had in pubs with other women. When he came to see us it was only for a clean shirt, a mouthful of food or to sleep like an animal for a day and a night. There was no laughing now. He went mad in a way, concentrating all his energies on flight; always moving, always drinking, always smoking, always running away.

While it was going on I was only half aware of what was happening. Snatches of conversation that I later pieced together, bits of fights and rows I'd only heard the tail-ends of. As an alternative to escape I quarantined myself. During my last two years at school I began to move into a stage of surly loneliness. I got up on my own every morning, ate my breakfast and cycled along the Hill to Wix's Lane. At school I kept quiet and out of trouble but underneath my crafty politeness I was becoming bitter and sullen. Every evening I did a paper-round and got paid seven and six a week for it. I fetched my sister from the nursery or from her school when she was older, and I watched over her until Ma turned the corner from the bus-stop and shoved her tired legs up the road, wading against the current. On Saturdays I went to the Old Man's, an ordeal that made me, week by week, more resentful, more ungracious. I'd been robbed of something. I could feel my brain stirring and no one was taking any notice. I was saying things and no one had time to listen. The world was treating me like a bastard, I knew it, and then I discovered I was one.

My father didn't trust me. I was about thirteen, too quiet and too sly. He never left me alone in his flat save once. I was in the bath and his telephone called him away for half an hour. It was the chance I had been waiting for. I stood out of the water and, still wet, went to his filing cabinet.

I found the pornographic photos first, but they didn't hold me long, that wasn't what I wanted. I wanted the marriage photos that I found in the next drawer. There was my father dressed up in a grey topper, everything, the bride in white lace, long gloves, smiling beside him, perfect, only it wasn't my mother. Other photos showed the same couple, two children later, girls. Somewhere I had two half-sisters. Those grown-ups never tell you anything.

I found the private address book next. My father's other family lived in Streatham, a mere cycle ride from Battersea. As far as I could judge they looked about the same age as my three brothers. I heard footsteps in the corridor. I shut the cabinet quietly, without panic, and slipped back into the bathroom, sliding my body into the tepid, scum-topped water. The yale key rattled into

the lock, the door opened and the Old Man came into
the flat in a bound, like the Demon King. He glanced
into the bathroom, surprised to see me still there.
'Come on,' he said, 'I'm in a hurry, you should have
been dressed by now.'

'I was dozing,' I said, and got out, hiding my body.

He went into the other room and I could feel him
running his eyes over it, seeing if anything had been
touched. I had a moment of intense fear; he might have
left cotton across the filing cabinet to see if I'd open any
of the drawers. He hadn't, not that day.

'What are these wet footmarks?' he asked.

'The phone rang when you were out,' I lied, 'wrong
number.' I said it quietly, just beginning to hate him
afresh for the new secret I'd discovered.

It was easy for me to unearth my mother's marriage
lines after that. They were in the underwear drawer in
her bedroom, under the white paper at the bottom.
They'd only been married that year. We were all
bastards, even my sister.

Before long I took my bike and went exploring in
Streatham. I found the house easily enough. It was big
and airy, posh to me, a proper house with a front
garden and a back. I found an excuse for knocking on
the door but no one answered and I never went there
again. I made sure my Ma knew I knew and though I
never said it openly I had the satisfaction of making
her cry. I didn't hold her hand or say it didn't matter,
not until years later at any rate. I just turned and
walked out of the flat with my nose in the air, sorry for
myself. I was a nasty bit of work and I would have
become much worse probably if it hadn't been for a
chance meeting with Bernard, in the street.

Bernard was standing right outside talking to a

couple of kids I knew, and I ran downstairs and joined
in. He had long trousers on, which we didn't, and he
looked better off than us. He was a good-looking boy
with a pretty mouth and wavy black hair. I'd seen him
running down the road a few times on the way to his
girl-friend's, running with gentle steps so as not to
upset his quiff, turning his head into the wind, keeping
the greased waves steady.

After talking to us for a while he went towards the
Hill, on his own. I ran after him and we walked along
together and we became mates even though he was a
full year older than me. It never changed after that.
There was something about Bernard.

I lived near the bottom of Lavender Sweep and
Bernard lived at the top, by the Common. He'd not
long moved into Battersea and that's why we'd never
met until then. His flat was bigger than ours and
much better to be in. It was airy and relaxed, at least
when Bernard was there. His mother was a nervous
woman and made anyone in her company feel the same
way.

When my mother did extra work, which was often,
Bernard and I would spend hours walking up and
down, talking. In winter we wrapped up with scarves,
in summer we sat on the coping or on the steps till well
past midnight, discussing what we would do if we had
money. We talked all the time, about anything.

Bernard was very good with people. They couldn't
pull the wool over his eyes but if he liked them they
could see it and he made them smile. He was witty too;
things popped out of him, ceaselessly. When we first
met and I told him that my Old Man was from Spain,
to show off I suppose, Bernard looked at me with a
straight face and said, 'Oh yes, what road?' I saw him
do it to other people too, he even did it to himself.

His father died that year and I went to the funeral. Bernard's dad had been a post-office clerk. As the coffin went down into the ground Bernard whispered, 'It's a dead-end that post-office work,' and then he cried.

So Bernard left school to help his mother. He wasn't specially good at anything but he liked printing his own photos in the bathroom so they got him a job as a projectionist at the Globe cinema in the Northcote Road, where the market is. It was a useless job and Bernard knew it, but he could earn more at that than at anything else and his mother needed the money.

I met Bernard every day once he started work in the projection box which was stuck onto the back of the cinema. I saw the films for free and waited for him so we could walk home together. Even then we wouldn't sleep but sat on the coping, or did something stupid, waiting for Ma.

Late one summer night when it was far too hot to go to bed, we brought the chairs and table down into the street and laid out all the tea things. Bernard and I had a real party going for Ma when she arrived home from work. We sat her down in the dark, lifted her feet up, and poured her tea. She enjoyed that and smiled at us in the lamplight. We stayed there until even some of the neighbours joined us. I don't suppose anyone in the whole street was asleep, it was so hot and sticky that night.

Two coppers walked by and stopped, looking us over as if we were green Martians, just landed. 'What do you think you're doing?' they said, all truculent. 'Where do you think you are?'

'We're a street party,' said Bernard, 'celebrating the late victory, only we're a bit late.'

Ma had to be really nice to those policemen before they would drop it and go away, but she was right really. It's as well to keep away from the law because once they've got their hands on you they never let go.

Uncle Dennis told me that he ran round a corner to catch a bus once and found himself in the middle of a fight between some coppers and some crooks. He was hit across the face with a truncheon, kicked in the back and arrested on the spot. It made no difference what he said. 'I looked like a criminal when I came before the beak,' he told me. 'I had bruises everywhere and a torn jacket. I got fined a tenner and reprimanded for being a hooligan.'

Bernard was a Catholic and a member of the Youth Club attached to St Vincent's, a red-brick church a couple of streets away from Lavender Sweep. I became a member too and went there with Bernard every Monday night. It wasn't a very good club, in fact it was lousy: long empty rooms, bare boards, table tennis, darts, shove-ha'penny and weak tea. We certainly didn't go there for the luxury, we went there for the girls.

The Youth Club taught us to fox-trot, waltz and quick-step, and that was useful, but the main game was trying to get the girls outside where we could attack them and squeeze their bodies, even though Father Ryan always sat right by the door to make sure that we didn't. He took a strong dislike to Bernard and me. Every time we went near a girl the hellfire switched on in his eyes like 'TILT' on a pin-table machine. Still the girls had to go home some time, and that's when we struck. I took those who lived on the other side of the Common and who were in no particular hurry to cross it. I always began with a girl who left early, and if I didn't do well with her I'd run back to the club before it closed and get another. Three in one night was my record and Father Ryan knew nothing about it.

The Youth Club certainly helped. It gave us the chance to touch the new flesh in the bosoms and buttocks of young girls—Margaret, Eileen, Sheila, Judy, Maureen, Pat. On occasion we were even allowed to stick our fingers up the marvellous and smelly orifice. We could prod thighs and handle tits in the moonlight of Clapham Common. We could do anything we liked except what we were dying to do. We could never actually get it in. It was one of the things that Bernard and I talked about endlessly. We were angered by virginity. We knew all the techniques, we read all the books, we looked at all the diagrams, black and white and coloured, but we couldn't get a girl to go all the way.

'There are hundreds, millions of girls,' I said to Bernard every night when I met him from work.

'Yes,' he'd say. 'And they're all hanging on to it like grim death.'

Before we could resolve the difficulty I was forced to concentrate for a while on something else. One day I went to school, the next, legally, I went no more. It was the beginning of 1950, I was fifteen. I was out in the world with no idea of what I wanted to do, and no skills to do it with.

I was hardly aware of leaving school, hardly aware of losing school-friends; Bernard was enough friend. But I knew nothing; worse, I knew I knew nothing. My father's world, however much I hated it, had given me a perspective. I could read and I could write and I could do my sums. I could care for my bike, I could bunk in at all the local cinemas, I could steal. I had a talent for wangling money out of most adults I knew and I could get my foot onto a dropped pound note before anyone else had decided whether it was an autumn leaf or a bus-ticket.

My teachers had sometimes talked, without hope, of

careers—a job that you took when you left school and
spent the rest of your life doing so that you were at
the top of it by the time you died. That was the goal,
the way to live. To put against that I had the example
of my uncles, my brothers. Good jobs, they seemed to
say, were reserved, in the main, for the classes above
us. It was better to take one job after another, keeping
yourself free of anything but the need for more money
next week, that was enough responsibility for anyone.
To follow this course it took courage, the courage to
scrounge whenever necessary. I looked at what my
teachers said and how they lived, I looked at the way
my uncles lived, and I decided to be free. My father
offered to find me a job on a national newspaper. 'No,'
I said, 'I don't want to be like that . . . a regular job is
prison.'

I took a long time starting work because I had no
idea what I wanted to do. My mother bought me a
second-hand suit, dark grey with a red stripe, but the
ideas didn't spring to mind and I moped about at home
for weeks. When I was nagged I went to the Globe and
hid in the projection box with Bernard. It did no good.
One day my family mobilised against me and told me I
had to find a job, any job. George was there and
suggested I help him on his greengrocer's lorry for a
month or two, till I found something better. And so I
started work.

It wasn't difficult. I'd often gone working with George
during my last year at school. George had married very
young, a girl he'd met at a Town Hall dance, right after
the war; now he had her, four kids and a shop in
Battersea Park Road. His greengrocery round covered
most of the streets along Lavender Hill and Wandsworth
Road and he had an old Commer lorry to ride the
miles. It was the oldest lorry in the world. Two or three

times a week, at four in the morning, we drove it over
to Covent Garden Market so that George could stock
up with fresh supplies. That was the best part of the
job, waking up in the dark, stumbling down the stairs
from the flat, still asleep, and continuing to sleep in the
warm petrol smell of the rattling lorry cab. Nothing
moved as we crossed London, the streets looked empty
and sick. The surprise came when we arrived at Covent
Garden and found that there were people alive after all.
It was all porters and lorries and handcarts and noise. I
loved it and with George behind me I soon became
completely at home there, finding my way confidently
from one wholesaler to another through tunnels lined
with sacks and boxes. It was a maze constructed of
cabbages and carrots, peopled by a race of swearing
and spitting men who charged at you with barrows
loaded with fruit and God help you if you didn't get
out of the way. The pubs were crowded, busy like
Christmas Eve, with giant porters straddling the pavements with pint mugs in their muddy hands. In front
of every pub was a rolling bank of half-warm, half-
cold air, impregnated with a bitter smell of sweat and
cigarette smoke.

As soon as George had compared prices and made
his choice he sent me back to the lorry to take delivery
of the stuff that he or the porters would bring. I was
pretty useful and could lift a hundredweight of spuds if
I had to. When the lorry was sheeted there was just
time for breakfast in one of the pubs, then suddenly it
was daylight and we were tearing across London again
to unload at the shop and prepare the lorry for its day
of deliveries.

Greengrocery is an adventurous trade. To judge
from my brothers' conversations they worked miracles
in the bedrooms of Battersea and Wandsworth. It

wasn't often that the four of us worked together, but occasionally Steve would take a day off from driving and Tim would get home at the same time and then the very look of the streets changed. The housewives would chuckle in their throats and open their windows, their wide bosoms unrolling like slow lava onto the window-ledges, and they would wave their arms and drop money down to us on the pavements below. A greengrocer's round that should have finished by noon would prolong itself into a smoky dusk. Many was the time I reclined all lonely on the lorry in the near dark, surrounded by Worcesters and King Edwards, banging the brass scales impatiently with my foot while my brothers were somewhere else, banging something else with something else.

We got fights out of it too. Husbands lay in wait for us, followed us, loitered in ambush on street corners. One of them once caught up with Steve. It was a Saturday afternoon in Sisters' Avenue. Fortunately for the husband Steve's right hand was bandaged that week where he'd injured it while trying to start the old Commer on the handle. Steve was disappointed, he quite liked a fight. He'd been well-trained in the army for unarmed combat and once told me that there were over twenty different ways of killing a man with your hands. George was in a house further up the street when the husband jumped Steve and all Steve could do was fend him off. I was on the lorry and pelted the man with spuds for a while but they only seemed to annoy him the more, so I ran for George. He rushed into the street doing up his trousers but I'd come to expect that. George got hold of the husband and flung him to the ground.

'My quarrel's not with you,' said the husband, halfway to his feet.

George hit him then, right in the face, with all the force of his fist. The husband fell over before he could get up.

'It is now,' said George. 'Leave Steve alone, his hand's broke.'

The husband sat in the road and felt the blood on his face with his fingertips. He didn't get up.

'You keep your brother away from my wife,' he said.

'You keep your wife away from my barrer,' said George.

The husband stayed where he was and we drove the lorry further down the street and carried on working.

'You spoilt my bunk-up,' George said to Steve and that was the end of it.

They were good sorts, my brothers, they didn't keep it all to themselves.

'Here,' said Steve one day as he finished packing an order into an old tomato-box, 'take this over to Mrs Waley's ... don't hurry back.' I was told afterwards that the woman had asked Steve to send me to her; she'd had all my brothers and only needed me to complete the set.

Mrs Waley lived in an ordinary terrace house in Fontarabia Road, but there was nothing ordinary about her. She liked sex more than food and she collected men like I collected marbles. About twenty-six years old, she had four kids and it looked like she'd started another. Her face was warm and kind with soft edges to it and she had blonde hair cut in curls about her face. She was sweet-looking, always cleanly dressed, and her christian name was Suzanne.

'Nice girl, do anything for you,' my brothers used to say as they took her vegetables over and disappeared for half an hour.

She opened the door as soon as I knocked and

looked at me gently, like a Cub-mistress welcoming a new recruit.

'Bring it through here, Mick,' she said and instead of showing me into the kitchen, which was at the back of the house, she steered me into the front room. She took the box of greengroceries and slid it onto the sideboard. On the other side of the partition wall I could hear her children whining and playing and throwing things at each other.

'Sit down here a minute and I'll get the money.'

She went out and I heard her go to the kitchen. I looked round the room but I'd seen it a hundred times before in a hundred other terraced houses in South London. It had the cold look of a room that is used only once or twice a year: christenings, weddings, funerals, Christmas. A three-piece suite, a sideboard, a couple of ugly pictures, souvenirs from the seaside, and net curtains. I expected to see my brothers peer in at the window but they didn't. They were shouting their wares further up the street.

I heard Mrs Waley go into the next room and give her children some sweets. They quietened down and she came into the front room and locked the door, smiling. She looked hungry. She sat down next to me and wriggled her bum into the sofa cushion.

'Now we're quite alone, aren't we?' she said and I remember she spoke well, in little precise sentences. She leant over me and kissed my face. It was good, very good, more especially because it was the first time an experienced woman had got her hands on me. She undid my shirt buttons one by one. There wasn't a hair on my chest and her breath eased up and over her bottom teeth as she ran a hand over me.

'You're lovely, Mick, so slim,' she said, 'such a smooth skin, there's a nice virgin feel to you.'

I blushed. My brothers must have told her, the sods. Nothing was sacred to them. Suddenly she seized one of my nipples in her teeth. I'd never had that done to me before and it gave me an erection like a girder. Her tongue began to move all over my chest, she shifted her head down to the flat of my stomach and I got panicky. I realised what she was going to do, I wanted her to do it, but I was scared of her doing it.

Still running her mouth and teeth over my stomach, she undid my belt and slid my trousers from beneath me. I raised my behind to help. Then she did it, licking up and down and bit by bit, nipping gently too with her teeth. Soon the girder was right into her mouth, as far as it would go and she didn't let it out until it was drained, exhausted. I stared over her bobbing head at the net curtains and watched people passing in the street. I felt somehow ashamed, I hadn't done anything. I'd wanted to, I'd even tried, but she had stopped me.

She raised her head and smiled at me again; it wasn't the same smile as before, this one was slightly crazed. The faint moustache of blonde hairs on her upper lip was wet and her mouth was slack, satiated, but her voice was as sweet and as trim as ever.

'Come along, Mick, your brothers will be worrying where you are,' and she began doing me up, like a mother dressing a child.

'I'd like to do it properly one day,' I said in a quiet voice, knowing well that I ought to make the most of Mrs Waley.

'That was properly,' she said, sounding rather shocked and pushed me roughly from the house. I forgot to get the money for the veg.

At first I headed away from the direction my brothers had taken, but after walking round the block a couple of times I caught up with them a street or two away.

'Hello then,' said Steve, leaning on the side of the lorry and grinning. 'How d'yer get on?'

'All right,' I said off-hand, 'all right.'

George came running up with an order. He threw the weights onto the scales and scooped up some potatoes. He'd forgotten where I'd been.

Steve said, 'He's been at Suzanne Waley's.'

George's head turned and a grin spread over his face, slowly, like each muscle was new. 'Has he?' he said. 'I don't blame him. It's better than the real thing ain't it, Mick?'

'Yeah,' I said, 'not half,' and I began to help weighing up the spuds.

I didn't know what the real thing was like of course, but I went back to Mrs Waley's in an attempt to find out. I walked up and down past her house for hours one afternoon hoping that she would open the front door to put the milk-bottles out and I could say that I was just passing. The door remained shut until I made myself knock on it. She must have had someone in there because she took her time in answering and her face had that same off-centre look that I remembered.

'Oh no,' she said, as if she were on the point of adding, 'I've only got one pair of hands, you know.' What she actually said was, 'Go away, Mick, there's a good boy, not today.'

I'd spent hours of preparation over the words that I was to utter as soon as I saw her, words that were going to carry me smoothly past the door and suavely into her bed, where she would discover what a fantastic lover I was. I had opened my mouth when she'd come to the door but I hadn't said anything except, 'Oh, er, hello, Mrs Waley.'

I couldn't stay in greengrocery for ever, and at last

George told me that I had to move on. I still had no idea what I wanted to do and so I drifted into another temporary job, this time in the local department store.

Arding and Hobbs forms the corner of Clapham Junction which is diagonally opposite the Falcon public house. They gave me an interview and the personnel manager told me about wearing clean shirts and ties, polishing my shoes and being polite to customers. I looked at a pimple on his nose and thought of something else while he talked. I don't suppose he believed what he was saying either.

'You seem a bright young fellow,' he said, 'your headmaster gave you a glowing reference.' That was rich. Woodsie only wrote reasonable reports so that he wouldn't look a fool.

They started me off at two pounds fifteen a week before tax and of that I gave thirty shillings to my mother. That didn't leave me a lot to play with but at least I had no fares and my Aunt Jane did lunch-times on the till in the staff canteen so I didn't do too badly.

I was put into the shoe department the very first day. 'Start at the bottom,' they said. The man who ran Shoes was called Hucker and the choosing of his nickname needed little imagination. Hucker had been in that particular job for a hundred and twenty years and he thought that staying so long in one place had endowed him with an impregnable superiority. Even people who had changed departments within the same firm had 'no stamina, no training ... fly by nights ... why, it takes years to learn something, that is thoroughly.'

I never saw Hucker laugh, never. He was a smirker though and that seemed to be his chief pleasure. His was a knowing smile, steeped in useless knowledge. The kind of smile that made you feel violent, that made you wish you'd been trained in torture by the Gestapo.

The job was pointless, all dusting and polishing, sorting laces, and stacking shoe-boxes in the storeroom. If I complained about the boredom I was told that all great men had had humble beginnings and out of acorns grew mighty oak trees. It was no good telling them that I wasn't a bloody acorn and that I didn't have the same lifespan as a bloody oak, that I only had one life and it was getting away from me. No, nothing I said made the slightest difference. They would just tut-tut and shake their heads and bring out another proverb. It was always the same, ask a tricky question and they would answer with a proverb; proverbs saved them thinking, proverbs made them feel wise and happy and left their lives unchallenged.

'You're too frivolous, boy,' Hucker used to say to me, 'too frivolous by far.'

I always gave him the same answer, it saved an argument: 'Yeah, it's the money, it's gone to my head.'

I never could understand why he took it all so seriously. He only lived in one of those mean little streets off the Northcote Road. As Bernard said, 'He's got nothing in the world to be serious about, his situation is laughable,' and Bernard was right.

I hated it. I began to see my whole life stretching away full of Huckers and shoes and stiff smelly feet with sticky socks creased in between the toes. I used to steam out of that shop like a locomotive at half-past five. Hucker used to call mine the cleanest pair of heels he'd seen all day. What a joker he was.

There was no point in going home after work. My mother was still out and my sister Evie always with Aunt Jane. I normally went to see Bernard at the Globe and chatted with him in the rewind room.

When Bernard got off early we'd go to my place, or
to the Youth Club if it was a Monday. We thought it
was a rotten life and told each other so. What was the
sense of working like that to end up like Hucker or
Charlie 'Spiffen' at the Globe? Where did life go? It
was going somewhere but it wasn't taking us with it.
Some people were getting more than their share and
we were getting less than ours, we were well aware of
that. We both had empty jobs; we knew nothing, knew
nobody and we weren't moving. It was dull and the
forecast was dull for the next sixty years. Between the
two of us, after months of talking, we had done very
little. All we had achieved was the making of a few
rules for living. The rules were taken from the strongest
characters, the kindest natures and the happiest lives
about us. Nothing was to be taken seriously; friendship
was to be given only to those who deserved it and was
to be a hundred per cent; above all work was to be
avoided because it was a living grave.

I stayed at Arding's very nearly a year and it
transformed me into a wretch. Hucker niggled me one
day and I forgot the golden rule of keeping my mouth
shut and doing what I wanted anyway. Hucker and I
had a flaming row, right there in the middle of the
shoes, the mirrors, the customers, the X-ray machines,
the shelves, the footstools.

'I'm taking you to personnel, I'm taking you to
personnel,' Hucker was screaming. Nothing like this
had happened in Shoes during his whole hundred and
twenty years in charge. 'I'm not standing for this, I'm
not standing for this,' Hucker was going mad. The staff
came in from the other departments to watch, the
customers were enjoying themselves. I wanted to leave
the shop altogether but Hucker wouldn't let go of my
wrist and he was a wiry old bird. We struggled

backwards and forwards, he pulling me towards the stairs that led to the offices and me trying to get to the nearest exit.

All those months of shoes and feet and Hucker had made me quite as angry as he was but if he'd let me go nothing would have happened. I remembered what Steve had told me about his unarmed combat training. When the enemy is pulling you one way and you are pulling against him, if you suddenly let your body relax you will both fall over. It's while you are falling that you can do the damage, bringing your knee up and your head down, using your weight.

Old Hucker never knew what hit him. I did it very well considering I'd only practised it before. I broke his nose and there was blood all over his face. He also got a nasty pain in his gut and his glasses were smashed.

When Ma came home from work I told her what had happened.

'Hucker pushed me about once too often,' I said. She looked grim and bit her mouth as she made the tea.

'You'll have to get another job straight away,' she said.

I didn't of course. I stayed out of doors, kept sullenly silent and spent my time at the Globe cinema with Bernard. But my family cornered me one Saturday and closed the street door and we had a good row about it.

'You're bone-idle,' Ma said, 'you don't want to work.'

I didn't answer; what she said was true. George leant against the door, pompous, grinning, self-important.

'Why did you go and leave Arding's?' said Steve. 'You had a good job there.' I looked at him. The beer had fattened and coarsened his face.

There were six of us in the living-room and I felt hot. Ma cleared the table of dinner things and went into the kitchen and carried the row on from there.

'Because he punched Hucker on the nose,' she shouted. Steve smiled at that. He was getting ready to go round to the pub.

'I didn't punch him,' I explained, 'I nutted him.'

'You get a job, Rothschild,' said George, 'like everyone else.'

It was none of his business, I thought. He didn't live at home any more.

'Piss off,' I said, brave really because George was strong and very handy with his fists. He once had a fight at Battersea Town Hall and put a bloke into Bolingbroke Hospital for six weeks.

George punched me in the kidneys and I fell over. It was difficult to breathe but Ma heard me cry out and came back from the kitchen. She didn't have to be told what had happened: Steve never hit me, only George.

'You bloody bully,' she said, 'just like your father. Go on, get out. I've enough to worry me without you causing trouble.' Evie began crying.

'He's too bloody cocky,' said George, opening the living-room door. He looked awkward and red-faced, a mouthful of gums.

'And what do you think you were at his age?' said Ma. 'Go on, get out.'

George went across the landing and down the stairs and Steve went after him. I heard the lorry start. I got to my feet and ran to the landing window, pulled it open and stuck my head outside.

'You old wanker,' I shouted as loudly as I could. I knew he wouldn't hear me, you couldn't hear a thing in the cab of that Commer truck once the engine was going. George drove off down the road towards Lavender Hill, the veg rolling about on the back of the lorry.

I banged the window down. 'He's a sod,' I told myself, 'a real sod.'

My Ma stood by the street door holding Evie by the hand.

'Your mate Bernard's been in the same job since he left school,' she said.

'Yeah, but he don't like it.'

'Who likes work?' she said. 'Do you think I like what I do? I've had a lifetime of it.'

'Yeah,' I said, not listening. 'I'm going to see Bernard.'

'Why don't you take your sister for a play on the Common?'

'I can't,' I said, and I ran down the stairs into the street.

I got out of earshot before my Ma could call me back. I turned the corner onto Lavender Hill and took a deep breath, feeling free, and allowed my body to drift into the Saturday crowds. There were hundreds of shoes rapping on the pavements and it was good to be away from the flat, from the family.

In the Northcote market I walked backwards and forwards in the gaps between the barrows, it looked like a kid's game but it wasn't. I came away with two oranges, one for me and one for Bernard.

A little way into the market, on the left, by the side of the Globe cinema, was a narrow wooden door set in a brick wall. Behind the door was an iron staircase, almost vertical, and at the top of it you could see lights flickering and hear the rough noise of the sound-track and the raised voices of the projectionists.

That was where Bernard worked.

Most projectionists are only just human. They live out of the daylight and their skins are green. Fresh air gives them asthma; on their days off they rush to other cinemas to visit other projectionists so they can chat about projectors, managers and usherettes, and when they run out of things to say they lean against the portholes and stare at films which they've already seen.

Bernard was the 'Third' at the Globe and his 'Chief' was a skinny man, all elbows and knees, whom we called Charlie 'Spiffen'. Spiffen was not his real name but Bernard loved to invent whole scenes, whole worlds, it was part of his humour, and one of the many places he had invented was the Roxy, Edmonton, where the Chief was Albert Spiffen. The Roxy was a vast cinema, a thousand-seater, with offices, broken-down machinery which was always being replaced, a randy manager and easy usherettes of all ages and sexual tastes. There was a disaster a day at the Roxy and Bernard was the only person in the world who knew what happened there. Every time I saw him, even after a short interval, he was bursting to tell me of the latest drama unfolding in Edmonton.

Charlie 'Spiffen' had thin greasy hair with dandruff in it like flakes of soap-powder. You could see his scalp through the hair, covered in blackheads. Any girl who liked squeezing spots, such as Rita the Gam, one of George's ex-girl-friends, would have had a lovely time with Charlie. He always wore a dirty brown suit with oil down the front and a dirty shirt with a small collar that was crumpled under a screwed-up tie of no colour. Charlie's skin was a wonder, it had a hundred tones of green and it was knobbly like a crocodile's. His assistant, the Second, looked like a terminal T.B. case.

Charlie was standing by the porthole when I went in, watching for the change-over dots. The Second was ready at the other machine, waiting.

I said, 'Hello, Charlie,' and he nodded at me. Bernard was rewinding the last spool. He looked green too, eyes asleep.

'Have an orange,' I said. 'I won 'em in the market.'

The Second came over with the reel that had just come off and put it on the bench.

'Do that one,' he said and as he went he pinched my behind.

'kin' watch it,' I said.

'He doesn't mean anything,' said Bernard; 'he goes out with one of the usherettes.'

'My Ma says I've got to get a job,' I said. 'I need the money. Something better than the three quid I got at Arding's.'

Bernard looked across the projection box and whispered, 'You'd better come with me, I'm going down the Festival Gardens, there's plenty of work there.'

The whole country was preparing that spring for the Festival of Britain. Every village, every town was doing something. The South Bank had been cleared of its bombed factories and a mighty exhibition was being held there to remind the world that the war hadn't completely finished us off, and the Festival Gardens, set in Battersea Park, was a part of this grand defiance. It was also exactly a hundred years since the Great Exhibition of 1851 and so we were all encouraged to celebrate our continuing existence if nothing else. Our slogan was 'Britain Can Make It', which survived only a short while before becoming, in Battersea at least, 'Britons Can Take It'.

Bernard was free that afternoon. I met him from work and we went upstairs on a 45 bus and sat at the front. The bus was empty and the conductor had to come all the way up there to get our money.

'Couldn't you soppy sods get a bit further away from me?' he said. 'Like on another bus?'

There was a cinema in the Festival Gardens, the Riverside Theatre it was called, painted pale blue and white with a big notice in black which told us that it was the 'Cinema of the Future'. That was where Bernard was headed, taking me with him.

'If we see anyone,' he said, 'put a year on your age, say you're seventeen and a half like me, then you'll get more money.' I was scared because I knew nothing about projection, but Bernard laughed.

'Yes, you do,' he said. 'Say you work at the Roxy, Edmonton, you know all the machines there. If you pretend the Roxy's real it will fool anybody.'

He was right, we got a job, one each. We found the managing director at the Riverside Theatre, the centre-piece of a tangle of electric wires, scaffolding and plywood. He was supervising a couple of workmen who were screwing down the tip-up seats. Bernard had no trouble with him because he really knew what he was talking about. With me it was different.

'And where do you work, young man?' said this big chap with a cigar and a deep voice.

'The Roxy, Edmonton,' I said, feeling like someone had put a whole suet pudding into my gut. 'I've worked there since I left school.' As I said it I hoped to Christ he'd never bought a pair of shoes at Arding's with me kneeling in front of him and shoe-horning them onto his feet.

'Would your chief projectionist give you a reference?'

'I should think so; he's never had a Third like me.'

'What's his name?'

Bernard butted in then, just to help me along. 'Albert Spiffen. He's my Chief's brother, that's how we met.'

'Oh really,' said the managing director. 'How interesting.'

'Albert's terrible,' I said, laughing at Bernard because I was on safe ground now. 'Generally drunk, which means that Gordon—he's the Second—Gordon and me, well, we do most of the work. I mean although I'm only a Third I have more responsibility than is normal,

it's extended my technical knowledge remarkably.'
That was a phrase that Bernard had told me to use.

It wasn't over. The man was no fool. 'What machines
have you worked on?'

'Well . . .' I cast my mind back to the changes Bernard
had made at the Roxy over the year. 'We started off
with these Simplex mechs, Peerless arcs and Westrex
heads, but they were so old there were bits falling off,
you know, the light was all yellow and the film kept
breaking in the gate . . . So we got the Kalee 21s, with
Lightmaster arcs, beautiful sound, they were painted a
kind of khaki colour.' I don't know why I told him
what colour they were, it was in the spirit of Bernard's
invention, I suppose.

The man nodded. 'Do you think you can handle a
stereoscopic link-up?'

I was stumped. 'Oh yes,' I said, looking at Bernard,
staring with fear, but Bernard only laughed and said,
'It's not much different from any other lash-up, it's
three-D, that's all. Two Simplex projectors with a
synchro-bar running between them, Polaroid filters on
each lens. The audience wears special Polaroid glasses
too, so what they see is three-dimensional.'

'Oh,' I said, and I pursed my lips with professional
understanding, 'is that all?'

The managing director laughed. 'That's fine. You'd
better come back in two weeks, I'll be ready for you by
then.'

We shook hands with him and gave good firm grips
and came away. When we were alone I turned on
Bernard but he was grinning.

'It's stereoscopic,' I said. 'I can't even say it, let alone
work it.'

He was patient with me. 'It's the same as any other
projector,' he said. 'I can show you how to do the job in

half an hour. Come round to the Globe every afternoon next week and you'll soon know as much as the Spiffens, Charlie or Albert.'

He was good like that was Bernard. We were too excited to go straight home. The managing director had promised to pay us six pounds a week, twice what I'd been earning at Arding's. I couldn't imagine having so much money. Bernard and I kept laughing at each other. Every time I said 'Six pounds a week,' they sounded like new words, out in the world for the very first time, and Bernard rolled over on the grass.

When I got home I told Ma I'd got another job and she asked me how much I was being paid.

'Four pounds a week,' I said.

She thought that was good. 'You'll have to give me two quid,' she said. 'I need that if I'm going to keep a roof over your head and good food inside you.'

I didn't say anything. I thought I'd done pretty well.

THE FESTIVAL

The Festival Gardens was a new world, bright and clean and good. Bernard and I moved from black and white into glorious Technicolor and everything snapped into focus. In the Gardens things were lit from the inside, shining; it was like a brilliant dream, whereas the edges of the world we knew had been worn soft and old and grey. In the Gardens we could do anything, we could dance, we could sing. We touched ourselves and discovered bone, muscle and brain.

There was grass and trim gardens all around. On the other side of the golden gravel road were wide steps, like a palace courtyard on a film set, and they led down to huge patterned esplanades and marble bridges. Painted kiosks stood by the path-sides and ice-creams, hot-dogs and Coca-Colas were sold there by youngsters in coloured bonnets. Beautiful girls, carrying baskets of oranges and dressed as Nell Gwynns in green silk frocks, wandered to and fro among the flower-beds. Out of work chorus girls in the main, they were something I'd never seen before, strolling casually like princesses, giving fruit and directions to people who were lost. I loved talking to them. They never rushed away and left you standing on your own, stupid and useless like a telegraph pole with your wires dangling. Everyone in the Gardens was friendly, it was over the rainbow and no mistake.

The men and women who worked there laughed at

their jobs, they scorned work yet they did it well. They wore outlandish clothes and didn't worry what others said about them. If you worked in the Gardens you belonged. Bernard and I took to it like a second home, it became more than a home. We talked, we joked, we listened, we chased girls, we were always up to something. In the Fun Fair the stall-holders shouted at passers-by and round every corner was a café with a terrace and screams of pleasure came from the Big Dipper. The staff-gardeners planted flowers from dawn till dusk and the fountains played day and night.

Soon Bernard and I knew everyone and they were all so different from us. They were travellers from a foreign land, they told their stories with exaggeration, easily, and their talk was the most wonderful thing. They spoke a new language and we had to learn it. New words, new ideas jumped out at us every day and we pocketed them and took them home to examine at leisure. Not one new phrase escaped us. The Riverside Theatre was a treasure house and in the land of the Festival Gardens our feet never touched the ground.

The theatre itself, our Cinema of the Future, was close to the Showboat, a replica of a Mississippi riverboat built on piers above the water, which the tourists could visit by walking up a gang-plank. It was painted in red and blue and played recorded organ music to us all day long. The back of the theatre, all underground dressing-rooms, wardrobes, corridors of concrete, was inhabited by a score of wild people, mainly actors and actresses, waiting for pantomime. Some of them performed in the various side-shows, some of them were door-keepers, some were usherettes. The Nell Gwynns changed their costumes there and Tiny Alf made them tea and pulled our safety curtain up and down. An artist named Quint kept his materials just inside the stage door. He was a small man, round-faced with a little beard and a beret, who earned his living that summer by drawing pictures and making silhouettes for the tourists. There was Benno too, a singer who had worked in West End musicals and panto. We called him Benno after a character in one of the films we showed, excerpts from the ballet *Swan Lake*; we knew that sound track by heart.

'Oh Benno, oh Benno,' it went, 'this was not always the home of owls and bats.'

Benno's job was to stride round the Gardens on six-foot-high stilts bearing a notice on his back which read, 'Don't drop litter.' Off the stilts he was quite small and quite mad. He once walked on his stilts across the stage in front of the screen, waving his hands at the audience and shouting, 'Benno, oh Benno, oh Benno.' All he said afterwards was, 'I bet they'll tell all their friends about three-dimensional photography now.'

Our chief of staff, in charge of ushers and usherettes, was a man called Scanell. A real professional with years of stage experience, Scanell was a female impersonator, a three-pound noter with a voice that he could project like a brass shell. He soon saw what a good audience I was, soon realised that I was fascinated by his language and use of words, and he never let the chance of a performance slip by. One day at the very beginning of the season, when I hardly knew how to operate the machinery, Mac, my chief projectionist, went missing.

'Do find him, dear boy,' moaned Scanell, speaking from his stomach. 'The show, you know, must go on, in five minutes' time. The curtain must rise, before it can fall.'

I thought I knew where Mac was—sipping beer

with a crony down by the ornamental lakes. I fled along the terraces and down by the esplanades, dodging at speed through the circling tourists. Mac would not be found. I was apprehensive at the idea of running the show by myself but decided I'd have to try.

I charged back up the hill and found Scanell standing at the main entrance, posed, forehead against fist, fist against wall.

'I can't find him,' I panted, 'anywhere.'

Scanell looked at me for an age; here was a bringer of bad news, here was a cream-faced loon. His lips tightened, he looked wildly about for an audience; there was none. He drew in a breath anyway, down as far as it would go, and he kept it there, roasting it. At last, after a long silence, he threw his hands away from his shoulders as if for ever, only to pull them back on sinews of elastic to caress his temples. He gave out a falling sigh and the voice he had been basting for so long issued hot from his chest.

'After this ... ah ... madness,' he said and he swept away through the theatre doors like Coriolanus leaving the gates of Rome. It was marvellous.

I went round saying, 'After this ... ah ... madness,' for weeks until I drove everyone witless with it.

These people, and their friends, used the theatre as a headquarters. Their letters were left there, they did their washing there, their eating, their courting. Some of them even slept there when money was short. They talked for hours over cups of tea and coffee, about the shows they'd appeared in and the things they'd done. Bernard and I couldn't stay away from them, we were always in or near the theatre, talking, watching, asking questions. We spent all our time together. I helped Bernard with his job and he helped me with mine. We became twin brothers, water became as thick as blood.

We thought the same thoughts, we breathed the same air, the same jokes made us laugh.

We always met at the beginning of each day and went down to the Park after breakfast to enjoy the emptiness of the Gardens and the feeling of ownership that came with it. We took our midday meal in one of the terrace cafés and we stayed late at night to eat in one of the restaurants. The side-shows were free to us and so was the Fun Fair but, after all, what we preferred was to sit in deck-chairs and watch the crowds come in through the turnstiles, thousands and thousands of them.

In a week or two I had completely mastered the job. It was easy, just as Bernard had promised it would be. I worked with Mac, a short, untrustworthy-looking little twister. He had fishy, blue, watery eyes and his breath stank putrid. Bernard worked with Roy, who was odd, silent and preoccupied, but very kind. He had scabby dry skin and a big ugly face, twice the size of any normal one. We all got on well together and our only boss was the manager of the theatre, the amazing Mr Bungey.

Bungey had blond hair, very carefully groomed. His movements were perhaps too meticulous to be graceful, but he made everyone else look clumsy. His skin was pale but gleamed with the attention he gave it; his cuticles were massaged to a healthy pink and his nails were bright. His nose was a little too large for his face but it looked dangerous, an instrument for rooting out lies and rubbish and spiking them to death.

Bungey was frightening at first but he was good to us, so good that I find it difficult to understand. Ten years older, he never reminded us of it. He had a mocking smile but he took trouble with us, explained things, though we often needed explanations of the explanations. Whenever he had a moment he would talk; there wasn't a word he didn't know, not a bit of human behaviour that he didn't seem to understand. He talked about the books he'd read, the films and plays he'd seen and the women he'd had. He opened doors and shoved us in.

As the season went on our fears wore off and we became close friends with Bungey and slowly learnt to know him. We discovered that he, who looked so well dressed, so wealthy, had in reality only one suit, which he pressed two or three times a week. He wore a white shirt, clean every day, with a stiff collar and a coloured tie, yet he possessed only two shirts and four collars in the world and often he wore them damp. He sported suede shoes and didn't consider it outrageous. He was spotless, neat and careful and he astounded us every day.

Nobody knew over the river like Bungey did. Often he took us across there with him. Twice we went to dinner in Chelsea together, at the Antelope, a fashionable pub with a restaurant upstairs. The tables were dark and polished, surrounded with bench seats, each one in an alcove. There seemed to be a mass of knives and forks and glasses by the plates. Bungey smiled, picked up some cutlery and said, 'Follow me.' I looked at the women there and thought how lovely they were, young and untired, smiling across the candles at their la-di-dah fellows, all dressed like Bungey, and I didn't know what to think. Them I hated, him I liked.

Bernard got on well with Bungey too, though in a different way to me. Bernard introduced him to the imaginary Roxy at Edmonton and the sex-life of the staff. They carried on long conversations about the 'problems' at the Roxy, such as whether the technicians and the managerial side really ought to come together socially. It went on month after month until gradually they had extended the world of the Roxy to take in everything, even the real world of the Gardens.

But it was with the problem of women that Bungey helped us most. Bernard and I spent a lot of our time gazing out of the window of the projection box and making noises at the good-looking girls as they went by, and at some of the not so good-looking ones as well.

'Crumpet will be the death of us,' we said, looking at Bungey and waiting for him to wave a magic wand.

Midway between the theatre and the Showboat was an ice-cream kiosk set in a diamond of grass, and in it lived four girls, art students. This was a type of girl that Bernard and I had never met before and he set his heart on Joanna, who was, of course, the nastiest one of the whole bunch. She was no beauty, with a strong nose and a man's jaw, but her legs were good and she had nice even teeth though her face wanted to be hairy. It wasn't her appearance that made me dislike her, it was her manner. She was full-time at Kensington Art School, she lived in a prettier world than I did and she had a hundred ways of making it obvious. I don't know what Bernard saw in her but he was always more serious about girls than I was. Perhaps, because of her age and her background, he saw her as a challenge; the type of woman that Bungey might go out with, and if Bungey could, why couldn't we?

We were always talking about her, how to make it happen. Bungey listened to us, smiling, standing by the mercury arc rectifier, looking mauve, like something from another planet.

'I go over there to the kiosk,' said Bernard, 'but after I've said "Hello, how are you? Nice day," and she's said "All right, thank you," what else do I do? I mean I can't say "How about slipping into something comfortable, like bed?" can I?'

Bungey raised an eyebrow and it encircled the whole situation. 'Take a book over,' he said—'read it thoroughly beforehand or the scheme won't work—take a book over and forget to bring it away with you. Leave it there a couple of days, and then, when you go back you can start talking about it. You won't believe how soon you'll be discussing things, life, art, sex, bed.'

He made it sound as easy as falling off a log. Bernard looked at me, I sucked in a cheek and shook my head. We didn't read a lot.

'You'll have to try,' said Bungey.

The Bungey Bunk-up Book Plan, as we called it, certainly started me reading. I read the whole of Battersea Public Library that summer and I wondered, as I read, if everybody had started serious reading the way I had and if those who didn't read got less sex than those who did. Bungey pushed me along hard. He always carried a huge notebook with different booklists in it and every now and then he'd flick over the pages, look at me and say, 'This one next, Michael,'—everybody else called me Mick—'and then this one.'

I didn't like all the books he made me read but I read them. I had so much time, waiting for Bernard to finish his shift, waiting to begin mine, sitting in deckchairs. I even read when I was rewinding. I liked Bungey's attention because by it he implied that I was as potentially clever as he was, I was only a little behind, it was just a question of the number of titles consumed.

But there was a big dark secret between Bernard and me on the one hand and Bungey on the other. It was something that we kept to ourselves, discussing it only behind locked doors or in the middle of windy commons. We couldn't have told Bungey, his eyebrows would have massacred us. The truth was that we'd never had a girl all the way, everything.

The thought chivvied us in our sleep, it halted the fork on its way to the mouth, it stopped the hand as it turned a page, it was an obsession.

Across the golden gravel road was a huge cafeteria with a wide terrace. On fine days Bernard and I ate there, looking down into the heart of the Gardens where the fountains played and the Nell Gwynns strolled and Benno yelled his own name. The restaurant cashier had once been a dancer but now wrote poetry every day, reading it to us just as frequently. It was awful stuff—Bungey called the woman a 'dyspeptic anapaest'—but we told her that it was wonderful and she often forgot to charge us for our food.

We'd been using the cafeteria for some while before we met the two manageresses. We saw them behind the counter occasionally but treated them no differently to anyone else, so it all began without us noticing. Before long Bernard and I knew them very well and were eating at the back of the restaurant in a pretty and private little garden.

It was furnished with a solid wooden table and matching rustic chairs; trees kept it quite secret from the road and there was a rock garden where the flowers were changed regularly by the staff gardeners.

'It's delightful here,' said the manageresses, 'peaceful and secluded.' It was. There was no view either, but we were eating a lot better than we had been and we decided that you couldn't have everything. We were wrong.

The manageresses were good-looking women though both over thirty, which was nearly dead as far as we were concerned. Miss Wise was lovely, like Maureen

O'Hara, with a good figure. She wore heavy make-up
with deep red lipstick, an inch thick. Miss Hobbes had
dark hair scraped back and wore glasses, but she was
very attractive with a kind and open face. I asked
Bungey whether he thought they were lesbians, there
were all sorts in the Gardens. He was a bit short-
tempered that day.

'I don't know,' he said, 'and I certainly don't have the
time to find out.' He went into his office and I leant
against the outside wall of the projection box, thinking.
As I stood there he jerked his window open. 'In any
event, Michael, it is beyond doubt that they are a trifle
odd.'

Then he popped his head back in and closed the
window. He always spoke like that, neat, the words
doing just what he wanted them to do and just when
he wanted.

In the private garden one day the manageresses were
watching us eating our dinner when Miss Wise said,
'How would you two boys like to come to the theatre as
our guests?'

Bernard was left speechless, which was rare. I'd only
been to the theatre twice with the school; both times it
had been Shakespeare and both times I'd disliked it.

'Oh,' we said, 'we'd love to go.'

We had no idea what we wanted to see and even the
Amusement Guide from the *Evening Standard* was of
no help. Miss Wise looked over my shoulder, very
close, and put her arm around me. I could smell her.

The manageresses decided that the best thing to see
was the revue at the Globe Theatre in Shaftesbury
Avenue. 'Afterwards,' they said, 'we can all have dinner
at our flat.' Dinner at eleven! Bernard and I looked at
each other and sucked in our cheeks and took it all in
our stride.

'Oh yes, that's fine,' we said.

The first thing we did was to rush back over the road and tell Bungey, tumbling down the steps into the office where he sat typing. He smiled his amused smile and then tried to make his face look innocent, but failed. He raised his eyebrows instead. 'Well, well, well,' he drawled, 'I expect you to tell me every detail, you know, every little thing . . . You've heard my adventures after all. A good story, mind, due preparation, none of that "*in medias res*" stuff.'

'Of course not,' said Bernard. 'What do you mean, exactly?'

On the night we were to go to the theatre we arranged with Roy and Mac to cover our shift and we dressed in all the finery we could borrow. We were to meet the manageresses at Shaftesbury Avenue and on the way we went down to the Gardens to show ourselves to Bungey. We stood on the path by the river and he walked round us and pronounced us splendid. 'I really can't wait until the morning,' he said. 'Don't you dare forget a single detail.'

I was surprised how good the show was. We sat in the circle and could see very well. Everyone was as dressed up as we were and we didn't feel a bit out of things. We laughed freely and Bernard was bright and bought some chocolates and passed them up and down as if he went to the theatre with girls every night of the working week. At the interval we went to the bar and we had beer, but the manageresses drank gin and orange. In the lavatory I said to Bernard:

'What do we do if they come on strong?'

'If they come on strong, we give it to 'em strong.'

'Yes,' I said, 'we give it to 'em strong.'

Afterwards we all caught a 19 to Sloane Square, for

135

the manageresses shared a flat nearby at the top of a house in a quiet road. As we went up the stairs Bernard pulled a face at me that meant, 'We're in it now.'

They had an enormous sitting-room, so long that I had to speak up to make myself heard from one end to the other. There was no central light hanging from the middle of the ceiling but five or six small lamps had been set up here and there along the walls. The floor was entirely covered by carpet, with no boards or lino showing, and there was a feeling of richness under the feet. There were books too and divans at each end of the room with bookshelves screening them. Through a door to one side was the kitchen, which was bigger than our living-room at home and nicely kitted out with all the gadgets and a fridge.

As soon as we got in they made us sit down and take our coats off. I didn't want to move about too much because my trousers were baggy and tended to slide down from under my belt, which was loose. The trousers were meant to be worn with braces and had no belt-loops.

'Do you want us to help?' asked Bernard. 'We're experts at cooking.' He could be such a fool.

'Oh no,' they said, 'everything's ready. You make yourselves comfortable. Drinkies?'

A big-mouth, I said, 'I'd love a Scotch.' Scotch was my Old Man's drink.

'Soda?'

'No thanks, they uses water when they makes it.'

That's what my dad always said. The Scotch went down onto my stomach like molten steel: we hadn't eaten since our tea-time in case we weren't hungry for their dinner-time. Bernard had worked that out: we would have looked very silly if they'd prepared a slap-up meal and we'd been full.

They disappeared into the kitchen, but not for long. Every few seconds they reappeared, dishes spinning like gyroscopes, steady on their hands. They arranged the table and Bernard and I smiled at them and nodded our heads. After a while I got to my feet and loafed around the room and looked at the books. I didn't recognise any but I remembered what Bungey had said about nobody being able to read all the books in the world or have all the women, there wasn't time enough, so I wasn't too disappointed, though I would have liked to have seen one book I knew.

'A charming little novel,' I might have said, 'but it sags a bit in the middle.'

Could those manageresses cook! Every time I thought we'd finished they brought out something new. I felt like a slave being fattened for the market. They gave us two kinds of wine which I didn't like at all, but by the time we got to the third bottle I couldn't taste it any more. Bernard did wonders, leaning back in his chair, holding his glass to the light and rinsing his front teeth in mouthfuls of drink. We got hotter and redder and the girls leant over us and touched our bodies when they talked.

Miss Hobbes had undone her hair and was looking mysterious with a cigarette-holder, but I still fancied Miss Wise more, drawn to her by the thickness of her make-up, the solidity of her lipstick. We seemed to sit at the table for hours. We finished all the bottles and the girls talked more and touched us more. I had an erection that was nudging the underside of the table and enjoying a life of its own. It was well into the night.

At last they said we should leave the table and Bernard lifted his behind and plonked himself back onto Miss Hobbes's divan, which was right by him. As he sank down he hit his head hard against the bookshelf and I thought he was out, but he grinned and rolled sideways. Miss Hobbes was all over him in a second and dabbed his head with cold water and undid his collar and removed his jacket. She put her face against his.

I stood up and I clutched the table but I couldn't hold it down, it swooped and swerved away from me.

'Oh Mick,' said Miss Wise, 'help me to the other divan.'

I did, stumbling and falling along the carpet.

She lay on her back on top of the bed and I sat next to her and a distant tiny and sober part of my brain wondered. 'Go slowly,' Bungey had said and I kept still, I didn't want to spoil a thing. Then I leant over and pretended to look at the title of a book behind the divan. That was my master-stroke because Miss Wise thought I was going to kiss her and her arms came up and circled my neck and pulled my face down and she kissed me. I'd never been kissed like that before, it took my breath away. The girls at St Vincent's had kissed me with pursed lips of dried apricot; this was real, this was tinned peaches in syrup. Her mouth was a powerhouse. It was wet and sloppy and strong. It could cover half my face with ease or creep behind my lips. The girls on Clapham Common had used their tongues like rashers of fried bacon gone cold; Miss Wise's tongue was gentle and inquisitive, electric, a warm quicksand. When she kissed me a thousand volts went whooping across my heart.

I came in my trousers then. I could have cried. I did. Miss Wise began to undress me. She must have guessed what had happened because I stopped her when she got to my belt.

'It's all right,' she said, 'I know, I know. We'll go to sleep.' And I did, straight away.

I woke up suddenly, every bit of me awake. I looked at the luminous dial of the watch that Steve had lent me. It was two-thirty. As I moved I realised where I was. I was inside the bed now with nothing on. Miss Wise, naked, lay beside me. She had slipped my trousers off, out from under the belt which was still round my middle, and I'd not noticed the going of them.

Miss Wise had fingers that matched her tongue. She traced firework patterns over my body with her red nails. When I was ready she pulled me softly on top of her and slid her legs up till she could hit me on the behind with her heels. Then she stopped doing anything except stroking me with one red nail.

'Have you done it before, Mick?' she asked.

I didn't want to look silly so I said, 'Yes, I have.'

'Everything?'

'Well,' I hesitated. Perhaps the truth would be best, for once. 'I mean no, not all the way.'

'Good,' she whispered in my ear and her hands came round and pulled me in and her heels beat me black and blue.

They threw us out soon afterwards because of the landlord and we crept off down the stairs. I was glad that Bernard and I had done it together. Those art students in the Gardens had better look out now.

The streets were silent and empty, the lamp-light shone up from somewhere far away down in the black tarmac. Sloane Square looked huge and without sides. John Law was waiting in a squad car and got out to ask what we were doing, and why.

'We've been to the theatre,' I said, 'and we're going home now, after a late supper with friends.'

I can't stand coppers and I wasn't going to let them spoil our evening by up-ending the atmosphere.

Bernard and I were quiet, brightening only as we approached the river. We began to talk; we went over the evening time and time again. Bernard told me what he'd done and I told him what had happened to me and where Miss Wise had put her fingers and her tongue.

We walked over Albert Bridge and up Latchmere Road to get back to Lavender Hill but we didn't go to bed. We were still talking as it became daylight, sitting on a bench on the first field of Clapham Common. But before then, coming across Albert Bridge, it had been so dark and so quiet that we'd stopped laughing to stand and look down at the river.

There it was, as black as the ace of spades, swirling along, fast, muck lying on the surface and moving silently. We were both dying for a pee and I wondered what would happen if we peed off the bridge; would we stop peeing this end before the first drop of pee hit the river? The distance looked so great that it seemed impossible to carry that amount of pee in you, but it isn't. We stood there for long minutes, the two of us, smiling at each other in the dark and listening to our pee rattle on the water.

The Tree Walk was a promenade of steps and planks rigged high between the branches of the biggest trees in the Park. It covered a good distance and I went there often, waving my staff pass and climbing into the sky without payment. I enjoyed the privacy of its branches and I loved watching the dusty crowds as they strolled, unaware, beneath my feet. I first kissed Sally up there, secretly, in the shadows of the green leaves; thousands of people below us and yet no one ever saw. Green lechery in a green shade; Sally had a lovely mouth.

Sally came to work in the ice-cream kiosk about a third of the way through the season. She was Joanna's younger sister, but more straightforward, prettier. She had recently left a convent school in Hammersmith and when the season was over she was going to a college in the West End to continue her education: languages, literature, shorthand.

Joanna was dark but Sally was fair. Her hair fell lightly to her shoulders, framing her face which was heart-shaped with a fine forehead and bright blue eyes. She walked well with firm strides that made her hair spring and her small breasts bounce. Every time I saw her walk like that the music of a military band came out of the air and every red corpuscle in my blood wanted to jump through my skin and fall into line behind her and march with chin up, arms and legs swinging.

Sally held her lips parted, her teeth pushing gently through. She never knew how much I loved those teeth because of what they had done to the shape of her mouth; she couldn't kiss with her mouth closed. She was proud and she was fresh, for me she had floated down from the tree-tops and had come to rest in the Tree Walk. I had never known a girl like her, all the others felt gritty to my hand compared with Sally. She looked so fragile that I wanted to love her the moment she appeared in the Gardens and I realised, for the first time in my life, that I was capable of doing anything to get my own way.

I dawdled in sight of her ice-cream kiosk, I logged the hours that Sally worked. I followed her to the bus-stop in the evenings, lurking behind the bushes like a dirty old man in a mackintosh. I peered round newspapers on her bus, I shadowed her to her house. I schemed, I plotted, and nothing worked. At last, when

I sailed into action, it was under the banner of the Bungey Bunk-up Book Plan.

It didn't work. I left a well-read volume at the kiosk for three days and when, heart in mouth, I went to retrieve it and to begin an irresistible discussion I found that Sally hadn't even noticed the book. Joanna had; she'd read it from cover to cover.

'Well then,' said Bungey smiling, 'it's Joanna you'd best take to dinner.' He could be heartless at times.

It was being in the Gardens that saved me in the end, just working in the same place. Knowing when Sally had her tea-break I strolled from the theatre at the same time as she left her kiosk, bumping into her casually, to ask her where she was going.

'Oh,' she said, hand to her hair, her expression anxious, 'to the ABC.' I went with her and that was how it began.

Bungey helped. Whenever I could think of nowhere to take her, afternoon or evening, Saturday or Sunday, Bungey was ready with an idea.

'Try the Tate, Michael. Fine art to look at, naked statues around you, right atmosphere ... good tea rooms too, quiet corners for the intimate kiss ... old masters, new mistresses, you know?'

It was a great advantage to have his know-how behind me. No one could explain the geography of courtship, or of London, like he could. He knew all the pretty pubs and cheap candle-lit restaurants within a ten-mile radius of Charing Cross. To Sally it must have seemed that I had been a habitué of fashionable London since the cradle, all on six pounds a week. I spent all my time with her; in a couple of weeks I had known her for ever. Every free moment we had was passed wandering across the London summer, ignoring the tourists, holding hands, kissing. June, July, August.

In August I got rid of my baggy trousers at last and now I wore fashionable ones, very narrow at the bottom. My mother used to look at me and shake her head.

'Where are you going then?' she'd ask.

'Oh, over to see Bungey, with Bernard.' Ma would smile. She knew there was a girl in it and she never said a word.

Bernard had a new one now, called Hilary, and she worked in the administration offices as a secretary. He bought a cheap ring and they got engaged but they were so serious about each other that they quarrelled all the time. The ring went backwards and forwards between them like a hand-grenade with the pin out, and Bernard and I spent as much time together as we always had.

Every Sunday morning, before work, I went to the Chelsea side of the river to meet Sally and then, holding hands, we went to find Bungey and Jennifer in one of his pubs. Bernard came too, with Hilary if they were talking, alone if they weren't.

It was a different pub every time—sometimes the Antelope, sometimes the Cross Keys, sometimes the King's Head. We sat in pubs with gardens too, drinking in the open air, looking at the Sunday morning people with their newspapers under their arms, and talking to Bungey about the things he'd done that week.

Bungey lived with Jennifer on a top floor in Old Brompton Road, above a harp shop. I liked Jennifer a great deal. She had short fairish hair, thick and bobbed, her eyes were fearless and her mouth attractive; the lines it had made for itself in her face told me that she was kind, and I looked for kindness on a face more than anything else.

I went to their flat eventually, with Sally and Bernard and Hilary for dinner. It was a wonderful evening, quiet, gentle, but lots of talking and laughing. I was so aware of sitting up there, high above London, listening to the remote noises rising from the city below. It was summer and warm; the windows were open and people were in the streets, strolling lightly dressed. The doors of the pubs were open too and men backed out onto the pavements, glasses brimming and wetting their hands. In Bungey's home I felt part of London, the whole of London, not just my little street on the other side of the river.

It was only a small flat, a sitting-room with bookcases and comfortable leather armchairs, a double bedroom, a tiny kitchen and a bathroom. It was clean as I had expected, but there were books everywhere, on chairs and under chairs, on the bed, under the bed. The books in that flat moved, they looked like they were in and out of the bookshelves all the time, settling arguments, ending discussions. There was green and silver Regency wallpaper in the sitting-room and the dining table was of dark wood, set off by a pale mushroom carpet. On a desk in the corner was a typewriter.

'How do you write?' I asked him.

'How does one or how do I?' His eyebrows attacked me but he smiled.

'How does anyone start?'

'You read and read, everything and everybody, looking closely, you become a spy, an eavesdropper, a gossip. Then you write something you think you understand, then you show it to your friends and watch them laugh or puzzle their brains. You squirm, you throw it away and go and get a job for ten years. Maybe you start again later, maybe you don't.'

Bungey's main interest was poetry; he'd written a great deal, all unfinished and none published. I read some of it much later and found it exciting but it was

over my head, like most of the music he put on the
record-player, like many of the things he said. He made
me well aware of how little I knew, how few places I'd
been, how many books I hadn't read, but it was
something else about him that worked on me more.
The way Bungey and Jennifer behaved towards each
other was something I had never seen. It was totally
unlike the rough camaraderie or exhausted indifference
that prevailed between the couples I had known. Their
manners were exquisite. Jennifer and Bungey listened
to each other, and they touched each other with care,
both with their words and with their hands. I loved to
see them saying goodbye when she came through the
Gardens. I came to understand that their leave-takings
were purposely prolonged, for the pleasure of it. I used
to watch them from the window of the projection box,
me drinking dark tea from an oil-finger-printed mug
and the man and the woman standing in the flat
streaks of dusk by the river, facing each other, touching
hands and smiling, planning the evening, the next day.
I wanted to be seen like that with Sally, and I wanted
to make whoever was watching think what I had
thought when watching Bungey and Jennifer standing
by the river. He had told me to spy on people, and I
did, and I started with him.

Autumn was coming, bringing with it more than the
threat of winter, October would soon shove its way into
the Gardens and boot the lot of us out of fairyland,
breaking the spell, scattering us for ever. Bernard
would be dragged off by the heels to do his National
Service and his mother would be left alone in her flat,
living on a widow's pension. I tried not to think of the
end. I would be back where I had been before. No job
and no idea of what I wanted to do.

A gloom came down over the Gardens. An empty
moneyless desert stretched out before everyone, it was
weeks before the beginning of pantomime. The weather
worsened, soggy leaves drifted into the doorways of the
Riverside Theatre and no one swept them away. The
fogs became damper and side-shows were dismantled.
The cafés were empty and a rough wind was clouting
the dying shrubs. Cement shifted, the terraces became
uneven and puddles deepened. The ice-cream kiosks
were boarded over and the girls were gone, Sally to her
college, Joanna to her art school, twitching for culture,
her big nose red with cold. The Nell Gwynns clustered
and shivered round the paraffin stove in Tiny Alf's
room back-stage where he made tea all day long in a
big brown metal tea-pot and put his coat along the
bottom of the door to keep out the draught. Benno
threw his stilts under the stage and leant against the
wall, staring across the grey grass towards the Showboat,
a *Mary Celeste* now with organ music. Bernard and I,
our shows cancelled one after the other, talked and
listened, storing our batteries with energy enough to
carry us through the dull months that were certainly
coming.

'The ship has struck an iceberg,' said Scanell towards
the end. 'Strike up the band, nail the colours to the
mizzen peak, women and children last, and let's get
drunk.'

He was right. Everyone in the Gardens was to have
an end of season party, why not us?

The cinema had been designed as a small Edwardian
music hall. Bungey decided to make the most of its
prettiness and to decorate the interior with greenery
and flowers. I was put in charge of acquisitions. There
was no shortage of creepers and potted plants in the

Gardens and I soon had a collection of flora to rival Kew. Those last days were foggy and I enjoyed an exquisite feeling of criminality as I crept along, stealing for the theatre. I had a moral right to everything I took, after all. I was rescuing a vital part of the summer, keeping it sacred from the hands of those November barbarians who would come after me to tear it all down, not caring one bit for the Gardens, never having loved them.

I took wicker seats, white iron garden chairs to put in corners of the stage and I had trellises with which to make arbours for lovers. I took signs, direction arrows, banners and flags. Nothing was safe from me. I prowled the Gardens by day, searching, noting, returning at dusk to bear away my prizes, slipping unseen through the uncrowded fog.

Provisions began to appear from the restaurants; tins of sausages and cylinders of cheese, big as garden rollers. Everyone was to bring a bottle on the night and we collected two pounds a head from the men to buy a barrel of beer and a crate of spirits. Above all the party must not run dry.

To the party we invited everyone who had used or worked in the theatre during the season—the girls from the ice-cream kiosks, Miss Hobbes and Miss Wise and their waitresses and the cashier who wrote poetry, people from the Staff Canteen, the beer tent, the side-shows, the man from the Tree Walk and a selection of 'shouter-outers' from the Fun Fair. For my own part I invited Sally and two of my brothers, Steve and George.

It rained all day on the last day of the Festival Gardens. The patterned esplanades and brick bridges were windswept and empty; Venice diseased. The dripping mist nudged bunches of dark leaves down the stairways and into the dirty water of the ornamental lakes. The light was weak and thin. Every one of our shows had been cancelled; the Cinema of the Future was slipping into the past. In the early afternoon I went with Bernard for one last stroll to say goodbye to everyone we knew. It was a mistake saying goodbye; it made us look beyond October and we saw nothing.

We began the decoration of the theatre as soon as our stroll was over, dismantling the screen first and putting it safely away. A trestle table was rigged along the front of the stalls and the food and drink was arranged on it. While this was being done I climbed a tall ladder and strung ivy across the proscenium arch, allowing streamers of it to trail down to the footlights. I placed my potted flowers and plants around the stage and used the wicker seats to make secret places for couples to sit in. Bernard worked on his own, running the cables for the P.A. system to give us music all over the theatre.

The party began early, there was nothing else that day. Everything was ready, everyone was there. Bernard brought the house-lights down to secondary, each person took a drink and we chatted politely for a while, about a hundred of us on the stage, waiting.

Bungey stepped onto a chair and made a little speech, then he raised his glass towards the Nell Gwynns, no longer in costume, and said:

'... and I hope this evening turns out to be as Restoration as the season has been.'

There were hoots of laughter and Bungey added, 'Shall we drink to that, and to each other?' And we all lifted our glasses and shouted, 'To each other, to us all,' and the glasses were emptied. Bernard increased the volume of the music and we came down the steps on both sides of the stage to begin the food and drink in earnest. The theatre looked like it had been taken over by a massive pantomime. The bright sparks had found the wardrobes and before long half the guests were wearing strange scraps of costume. I had always wondered what happened to the company of a show after the final grand finale; now I knew, for I was on the other side of the curtain at last, the audience had gone home, and the real party had begun.

For a while at least I wanted to watch and I wanted Sally to myself. As the drink ran more freely so more of us changed our clothes for costume and soon no one was dresssed as he had been at the beginning of the evening. Scanell became a woman. He began as an usherette, wearing a mob-cap, but he became several things in the next hour or two. It was difficult to keep track of anybody that night or to know who or what they were. As the evening went by individuals became less distinct, less separate, they melted back into one colourful mass and the colours slowly became darker and darker, like a child's plasticine too much mixed.

Couples detached themselves though and sat in the love-seats I had made. Some were in the auditorium, eating, drinking, holding hands, talking. Others had their heads together, their arms slung heavily round their partners' necks, kissing hard, kissing goodbye.

Joanna got drunk early. I saw her sprawling in the stalls, her legs draped over the row of seats in front of her, her head lolling. Quint, the randiest man in the world, roamed down the edges of the party and spotted her. He got down on the floor and wriggled along under the seats, emerging slowly between her legs. He began to mouth Joanna softly in the crutch, holding her thighs open with his furry little hands. She came awake with a growing scream, sawing her legs with pleasure, entangled herself in the tip-up seats and fell sideways to the floor. Quint leapt to his feet and shouted so we all could hear, 'I am the world's greatest

muff-diver,' then he followed Joanna down, out of
sight, between the rows, and they stayed there.

But the panto people held the centre. The drink got
to them, so did the feel of the stage beneath their feet
and the clinging costumes and there was no resisting,
they were drawn into their routines. Everyone danced,
everyone sang, everyone did their turn. We whistled
and applauded, drunk and proud.

Near midnight I went down to the dressing-rooms
under the stage and found a Nell Gwynn on her knees
in front of a lavatory, moving her head like a Muslim
at evening prayer. The place reeked of her stomach
and she had a spray of bright vomit across the front of
her dress, flowers for a wedding. The echo of her
moans rose from the pan and made my own stomach
falter and glide. Bungey was there with her, trying to
help, but she collapsed boneless to the floor, begging
for death.

On stage couples began to sneak away from the main
body of dancers, disappearing upwards to the circle or
gallery to be alone. Mac, small and slight, was borne
away by Marie, an usherette constructed like an Aztec
temple with terraces of fat spreading out from her
centre on every level and in every direction. The
whites of her eyes strongly tinged with yellow lechery,
she took Mac to the gallery and rolled onto him. I
poked my head over the top of the stairs and looked
across the carpet, but all I could see of Mac, sticking
out from underneath Marie's flesh, were his shoes,
pathetic witnesses to a small suicide on the edge of a
vast ocean.

Scanell ran up from the dressing-rooms. 'Holed below
the water-line,' he shouted, still drawing on his experience with sailors. He had discovered a flood beneath
the stage. A tap had been turned on to clear away the

Nell Gwynn's sick and it had been left running. The water was spreading and beginning to climb the steps into the auditorium. 'Man the pumps,' shouted Scanell and began organising brooms and buckets. Benno would not be organised and, serenely drunk, wandered into the flood for the fun of it. Bernard pushed him to dry land, telling him to get back onto his stilts, out of harm's way. That was a bad idea and Benno acted on it. He pulled his stilts to the stage, clambered up, with help, and stood high above us, swaying neither to left nor to right because we held him steady.

'Let go below,' he called, 'let go the stilts!' We let go and he remained vertical for about a second, smiling down on us with a smile that forgave us for all our doubts, then he fell forward, he and his stilts together, quite rigid, like a corpse from a cupboard. My brother Steve, easily as drunk as Benno, tried to save him, but they both tumbled down into the orchestra pit, crashing arms and legs. Only Steve got up. I never saw Benno again, that evening or ever.

After the flood the noise rose and Bernard notched up the music to keep pace. Small parties were being held within the framework of the main one. Groups were talking wisely in corners and dressing-rooms. I saw Bungey in his office, bedding down the sick Nell Gwynn girl.

'Always keep something for a rainy day, Michael,' he said and he turned his attention to a young actress whose eyes were so glazed that I couldn't see into them and she couldn't see out of them.

I felt glazed myself, so I took Sally out from the noise to the strange and special quiet by the Thames. The fog had settled along the river and had cut off all sound and light. There was nothing to be seen but fog. The Riverside Theatre was floating above the Thames, a busy world of its own, warm, separate from the rest of the universe. I could hear the water lapping against the embankment and the voices of other couples, out there in the night.

I took Sally to the railings at the river's edge and I leant against them. I had my arms round her and she fitted under my shoulder. I slipped my hand under her hair and touched her neck. I pulled her round to face me. Until now Sally and I had only kissed and held hands. I was frightened. I wanted her badly but she was a shy girl and I didn't want to scare her away. I tugged her into my body and her hard pelvis clipped itself onto me and I rested my chin on the top of her head. We stood there not doing anything or saying anything, pressing our bodies together. I was trembling. I kissed her again and again and again, on her open mouth.

While we stood there Roy floundered into the projection box and we could hear him among the machinery. Roy was normally a quiet man, a captive of the dim-lit world of brick-built cinemas, but the Festival Gardens had worked a charm on him. The night of the party had seen him explode and set forth on a demented pursuit of women, all women; he had danced through the hours of the evening, flailing his arms and legs against the music, daring the rhythm to coincide with his movements. Now he was blind-mad drunk and I could hear him with a spanner. I wondered if he was breaking the projectors. Perhaps he hated the machines for all the years he'd spent tending them, for the way they'd kept him locked in darkness out of the sight of women. I crept nearer and looked through the window. There was a light inside and I could see that he had undone the mountings of one of the projectors and had swung it round to point away from the screen and towards the Thames. Clumsily he threaded a reel of *Swan Lake* and struck up the arcs. He switched on, turned up the sound to the maximum and suddenly Von Rothbart, Odette and Benno, the real one, danced onto the fog, a hundred feet high, out in the middle of the river. It was the strangest thing I have ever seen. 'Oh Benno, oh Benno, this was not always the home of owls and bats.'

I clung to Sally and stared. We weren't the only ones to be drawn by the sound of the music, louder even than the party inside. Bungey and Bernard came out and we watched the dance together, knowing the music note by note, knowing the steps and the dancers and knowing that this was the last time we would see them. We were bewitched all of us, for a minute, seeing them on such a screen, and we didn't look at each other.

There was a hiss as the arc lights extinguished themselves and the dancers went down into the river. Roy was asleep on the floor between the two projectors with a big smile on his big face. I got in through the window and turned off the power and put an overcoat over him so that he could sleep undisturbed until morning.

It was quiet. Only a few figures were still on their feet, tired, staggering. George had his arms round a woman, he wanted to take her back to Lavender Sweep. He had come to the party in a dyer's and cleaner's van, tall and narrow, and he offered to drive us all home in it. I rounded up volunteers and we decided to load the van with drink and women and finish the night off at home. We all had girls. I had Sally, Bernard had Hilary and Bungey agreed to come along with the Nell Gwynn if she was sober enough. Steve, we supposed, had already gone to warm sheets with a warm girl.

I did the rounds to make sure the theatre was safe from fire, and I looked at the building for the last time. It was silent; everywhere I went there were couples sleeping in each other's arms, wrapped together with strands of costume. Better to lie in comfort than walk a girl home in the cold fog.

In the upper reaches of the gallery I found Quint, stranded, his body stretched out quite naked but for a large brassiere and his socks and shoes. The little imperial beard pointed to the ceiling.

The fog had thickened and we didn't know where to go for the van. We wandered in a swirling darkness, holding hands as legionnaires do in a desert storm, so that we shouldn't lose one another. In the end we found it by accident, clambered in and stood there, tipsy, clinging to the coat-rails above our heads, like revellers in the last Underground train on New Year's Eve.

George was driving. We should have kept an eye on him. He was drunk and we knew he was, but then we were all drunk. Suddenly the old van tumbled through space, downwards, a whole foot, terrifying; the girls screamed, George whooped and sniggered, his head swaying. Wheels spinning, the van began to bump regularly and fast, falling, picking up speed. My stomach shrivelled and I sobered in a second, realising that we were dropping down the wide shallow steps that led from the theatre to the long ornamental lakes, and that the lakes had no protecting walls around them.

I stopped George by putting my hands over his eyes and he collapsed giggling, long enough for me to get out into the fog and set us on a new course. This did not make things easier. Owing to the complicated geography of the Gardens we could only get back to the road by following an intricate set of narrow paths which wandered between the flower-beds and the abandoned side-shows. George thought this was wonderful. The van was low-geared and he shoved it into first and let it chug along on its own, walking beside the radiator and patting the bonnet like a pet dog. The girls, imprisoned in the driverless van, screamed as it left the footpaths at every bend and ploughed across the flower-beds like a tractor.

To begin with we shouted and cursed at George, but eventually we surrendered to him. We had plenty of whisky with us and we began drinking it to keep warm. The girls behaved as badly as we did, jumping in and out of the van as it crawled along, picking flowers, pulling down signs and loading them into the moving truck, working clumsily, laughing, like dustmen merry at Christmas.

We didn't find the main road until daylight when, groaning on its springs and leaning at a shipwreck angle, the van limped into Albert Bridge Road. By this time George had disappeared underneath a funereal weight of flowers and Bungey was driving. It was amazing, it still is amazing, that the van struggled up Dorothy Road, the steepest hill in Battersea, but it did. We climbed the stairs to my place, stumbling and dropping bottles. We arranged our trophies with care, flowers were tucked behind pictures and behind mirrors, they littered the floor, as did bits of machinery from the Guinness Clock and sections of the Emmett biplane. We sat and looked at each other, sheepish and exhausted, while the oblong of window gradually lightened. Finally we had one last drink, toasting ourselves in bitter whisky, and then crawled to bed in pairs, weary with pleasure.

Sally asked me to leave her alone at first and I got into bed promising not to touch her, knowing such promises are never kept. She must have known it too.

Her face looked worried as I began to make love to her, slowly, as gently as I could, though it was difficult because she wanted to keep her clothes on, to protect herself. I touched her carefully, trying to remember everything I'd learnt, though the need to have her was so powerful that it frightened every other thought out of my mind. The sun was up and her hair shone and her mouth was open and she closed her eyes and let me. I felt awkward and I knocked her knees with mine but she kept her eyes closed and her body was hard and tense. It hurt her, she said, but it got better and she made those noises and we folded ourselves together. I did love her.

My mother was shocked into silence when she got up that day. Our trophies were everywhere and under-foot. She walked slowly round the flat and counted the strange heads on the pillows. Bungey and Bernard were in one room with Hilary and the Nell Gwynn girl, George with an unknown waitress in his arms was in the put-u-up in the living room, and Sally and I were squeezed into my narrow bed.

Ma took it all in her stride, made my sister's breakfast and then went down to the Junction to buy the Sunday newspapers. In the afternoon, when we started coming alive and sticking our yellow faces out of the sheets, she made us something to eat and sat there and laughed as we told her the story of the party.

But when, earlier and still in Sally's arms, I'd first come awake, I'd opened my eyes and found my mother gazing down at me, thoughtful, but she'd only said, 'Mick, do you think I should make the girls a cup of tea? They could probably do with one.'

'If you like,' I'd answered and I'd gone back to sleep.

WAR
IN KOREA

It was a foul winter. The pavements were wet, and soggy newspapers sprawled in the gutters. Green oysters of phlegm squirmed underfoot and the sound of coughing and dying came through closed doors and windows. Sally was in her college, Bernard was a soldier and had been taken to Gloucestershire to train. Bungey found a job in the Savoy Hotel and I stayed at home, sulking, angry, not knowing what to do and living off a few pounds that I'd put by. Everyone else from the Gardens vanished into thin air.

I went to see Bungey sometimes. He worked all night, from eleven in the evening until seven the following morning, balancing out the totals in the day accounts book. He spent his nights with two old men at the top of an iron staircase in a dingy brown office hidden in the heart of the hotel. Perched on tall stools like clerks on a Christmas card, they added up figures, lips moving, hour after hour.

It upset me to see Bungey in such a job even though he said it suited him for the time being and allowed him to write. I was wary of all jobs, but especially those that were taken for the time being. I'd talked to many who'd been stuck in temporary work for thirty-forty years. To me it was an end, it was worse than selling shoes in Arding's.

October; the old dullness wriggling like a maggot, a lonely dullness too without Bernard. I wandered round

London like a ghost, self-pitying, dreaming of a previous existence. I thought of Bernard charging a sack of straw with a steel bayonet and polishing his boots till he could see his face in them. I thought of Bungey marooned on a stool, adding up columns of figures while the rest of London was asleep.

I went to see Sally at her college. I met her lunchtimes and when she finished in the afternoons. At the beginning I thought she would save me, but there were too many new faces around her. Soon we couldn't talk.

Every Friday dances were held at the college and I went to every one for a month. Sally enjoyed dancing, I was hopeless. I wanted to stand or sit in a corner and talk, but there were dozens of young men who could dance as well as she could. They dressed in tartan waistcoats and clean flannel trousers, they had polished fair hair and they pronounced their aitches, they discussed the parties they'd been to and where the best jazz clubs were. I became angry every time I saw Sally and she got bored walking in the cold with me when the college was so warm and there was always someone to drive her home in a car.

Martyn MacQuarry was the enemy; he was close to Sally, close as skin. I went to the college once, unexpectedly, and saw him coming out of the main entrance with her, arm in arm, laughing, him with his chicken's arse of a mouth. I could tell, just from seeing them together, even at a distance, that it was all over for me. Just the way their bodies touched was enough.

Sally saw me as I turned on my heel and went back round the corner. I caught a glimpse of her raising her hand to her hair, worried. Even that gesture hurt. I wanted to kill MacQuarry for having the things I lacked, the accent, the confidence, tartan waistcoats, the car. I ran for a bus and jumped on at the lights and sat at the front, upstairs on my own, and I cried, a suave man of the world.

I got off the bus at Clapham Common and walked the length of it swearing the whole way. I hadn't been indoors long when Sally knocked at the door. I was pleased to see her, it was kind of her to come at all. She knew better than I did that it was finished; we went into the bedroom together and that was the last time.

Steve hadn't gone home with a girl after the party in the Gardens, he'd spent the night in the open and it had nearly killed him. He'd got badly drunk that night, like he did every night, and he'd lost his way in the fog, falling over at last and sleeping where he fell. The cold woke him the next morning, soaked through and stiff, lying under bushes by the river like a metho. He got hold of the railings and pulled himself upright and reeled away to the nearest pub where he filled himself with whisky, hoping to warm his body back to life. He didn't get home to us until closing time that evening, still drunk. He didn't get up the next morning and in a sense he never got up again. Another driver came and took his lorry from outside and drove it away. Steve got worse, we called the doctor and he was taken to hospital with double pneumonia. He stayed there for six weeks.

Juno loved it. She got out of bed, painted face-powder over the grime and went to the hospital with a handful of grapes, a handful of flowers. Every time I went to see Steve she was there, roosting on the end of his bed, like a crow eating flat cat on a main road, hopping and pecking. But I didn't go often because I never found the person I'd gone there for. 'No resistance left,' the doctors said. Steve lay motionless in his bed, his eyes open and smeared with pain, his face covered with a thick rash, not hearing Juno's voice as it went on and on.

I hated the hospital, I hated the smell and the tepid bodies that lay stupidly in the wheeled beds waiting to be pushed away. I hated the doctors too, peering at me like I was already dead, and the nurses shunting the patients up and down with a bitter gusto, banging them into line like dustbins for a rubbish chute.

When Steve came out we brought him home in a taxi and took him to Juno's place, though he hadn't lived with her for months. She rubbed her hands and said no one else was going to look after him. Steve stayed behind his eyes and said nothing. I would have done anything for Steve, he was everybody's favourite, but there was nothing I could do. He'd gone somewhere else. He dozed through the days and took sleeping pills like sweets, escaping from Juno's voice and the smell of three kids. His mind slipped. He had always been slim and attractive, a mover; now he was fat, gross, ugly.

When he came out of bed it was worse. He was unrecognisable. He walked badly, slowly, shuffling his feet, his face puffy, extinguished. He would walk no further than the Labour Exchange where he picked up his money, then he took it straight to the Prince's Head to spend it. I sat with him sometimes in that pub but didn't stay there long, I lacked the courage, the generosity, the love. Men sneered at Steve behind his back and he didn't notice. When someone phoned the NSPCC at last and they took his kids away he didn't notice that either, at least he didn't show it, he just took to his bed.

He made one last attempt to get back to work, but it didn't last. His lorry was stolen on the road when he was drinking and he was sacked. Some of the load, cigarettes, turned up in the Battersea pubs and the law questioned Steve very closely. They asked me questions as well and though it was true that Steve did have too much money at the time he was not charged. After that business Steve moved back in with Ma and Juno went her own way. He talked to no one now and ate little. We could nag him for hours but it made no difference, he was a zombie with dead eyes.

Six weeks after the end of the Gardens I ran out of money and took work as a messenger, hoping that such a job would help me to avoid any new lurking Huckers. On my first day I was put into a bare room behind some offices to pack leaflets and forms into bundles for delivery to various parts of London. In the afternoon they gave me fifteen shillings, a list of addresses and several hundred brochures. I did two deliveries in Baker Street and was on my way down to Kennington when I got off the bus at Vauxhall for a breather. I walked onto the bridge and stopped in the middle to look at the water. I thought about all the people from the Gardens, I thought about the men and women I'd seen that morning in those offices and I thought about going back there the next day, and the days after that. What would become of me, what would I turn into?

I felt my anger rising. I resented the life that was offered me. I let the brochures fall from my hands into the Thames and watched the splashes with contentment. I kept the change from the fifteen shillings and took a bus home. I never went back to that job and I never heard from them.

November. It was my mother's turn to go into hospital and I stayed home to look after my sister, who was still only eight years old. I also cooked meals for Steve.

I was in trouble. With my mother and Steve both ill there was no money coming in and no likelihood of any. In desperation I thought of taking lodgers. I decided that if I tidied the place up and polished the lino I could let two of the bedrooms and survive on the rents. I kept one room back for Evie and Ma to share and converted the sitting-room into a big bedroom, moving myself into the same room as Steve. I didn't like it—Steve smelt of drink, sweat and sleep—but I did it because it was Hobson's.

It was easier than I'd hoped. I put an advert in the window of the nearest newsagents and I went to the office that found rooms for the students of Battersea Polytechnic. I began business with three students sleeping in the front room and I soon had two working-men lodgers besides. They were as happy as bugs in a bed, got their own breakfasts and ate in cafés and fish-and-chip shops the rest of the time. I made enough to live on and some weeks I was able to save a pound or two.

I liked it. Independent and earning well, I felt like a rich landlord. I had to do the washing up, the housework, the shopping, and put Evie to bed when Aunt Jane was working, but I got in front with the rent and the insurance payments and during the day I could read or visit museums and galleries. It was certainly better than working.

My mother was in St James's, propped up in an iron bedstead with a tube up her nose and her face shrunk to nothing, like a head-hunter's trophy on a stick. Her eyes were as big as saucers in her tiny face and wisps of grey hair fell across them. Her hands were knuckles and sinews only. The change in her, and in Steve, made me angry, I wanted to smash the hospital, punch those arrogant nurses. My mother had changed so much, craftily, behind my back, while I'd been looking the other way. I don't suppose her own dad would have recognised her if he'd come walking down the ward, just as she and Gran hadn't recognised him at Roehampton.

I got Steve out of bed once and took him to visit her in a taxi. He couldn't walk very well, he hated meeting strangers and it had become more and more difficult for him to go out anywhere. It took all his remaining shreds of courage to walk down the ward. He pulled his last cigarette from his pocket. It was bent and screwed up, nearly broken. He held it in front of his eyes and looked at it. He tried to straighten it with his thick, unsure fingers, but they trembled and I did it for him. He put the cigarette between his lips and shambled along, looking the wrong way as I guided him to our mother's bed. By the time he sat down the cigarette had drooped again and I laughed although I knew it was cruel. My mother laughed too, but when she looked past the cigarette and saw Steve she twisted her head the other way, without a sound, and her small face became covered with tears. I didn't bother to take him again.

December. The doctors sent Ma, convalescent for three months, to a nursing home in Bournemouth. This left me with six people to make Christmas dinner for: Steve, Tim, who would be home for the day, Evie, and the two lodgers who had nowhere to go, Big Mick and Brassic. I expected the Old Man too; he always appeared at Christmas, arriving once a year like a wavering Catholic doing his Easter Duties.

I took a couple of pounds extra from everybody and I bought all the usual things, dates, nuts, fruits and cakes and crackers. I planned to cook a turkey with roast potatoes and brussel sprouts and to buy the pudding.

On Christmas morning my brothers and uncles always went down to the Falcon and met their friends.

Uncle Ned and Joe came in early to call for Tim and
the three of them coaxed Steve from his bed, dressed
him and pushed him to the pub, the two lodgers
tagging along behind. Bernard was on leave and I was
cheerful because of it. I knew I would be busy all
morning, but the afternoon and the evening were for
Bernard.

I got on well with the cooking and I timed the meal
for half an hour after pub-turning-out time because I
knew the men would stand for ages on the pavements,
talking and wagging their fingers at each other. I
waited for a long while. I pulled a few crackers with
Evie to keep her occupied but my turkey was spoiling.
I stuck my head from the landing window but there
was no one in the street. I waited a few more minutes
and then I ran to the bottom of the road to see where
they were.

When I rounded the corner I discovered my family
scrapping across the length and breadth of Lavender
Hill. Except for the small struggling figures the road
had an epic Christmas Day emptiness to it. There were
no buses, no cars and no pedestrians. The tram-tracks
gleamed alone and dipped away in a distant perspective.
A snappish wind flicked the dust of the two bombed
sites on either side of the wide road, but I had no eyes
for any of that. There was a fight going on and my lot
were in the middle of it, everywhere.

Tim had a fellow in the doorway of Ford's sweet-
shop and was pasting him up and down like a poster
on a wall. Every time his adversary tried to fall over
Tim propped him up and hit him again. Joe was
chasing someone towards Electricity House. He tripped
him as he ran and the man went sprawling on his face,
his arms spread, his Christmas bottles smashing in his
pockets, and he cried out as bits of glass went into his

thighs. Uncle Ned was cornered in one of the alcoves of the bombed-out Pavilion cinema; two men were hitting him and he wasn't doing well. Joe saw his father and ran over to him very fast with both fists held in front of his body. He rushed full-tilt at one of the men and I heard bones breaking in the face. Ned gave the other one a beating and he ran away up Eccles Road.

I caught sight of the Old Man. He was standing on the kerb, guarding the drink the boys had brought back to have with their dinner and watching Steve. Steve could no longer move like he had once, but he carried so much weight with him that if he did land a good punch it could kill. He was standing solidly in the middle of the tram-tracks, hitting some youngster on the head, down into the ground like he would a nail, bang, bang, bang. A ginger-headed man from the opposition ran behind Steve, pushed him over and began kicking him in the head. Steve couldn't get up but the Old Man grabbed a quart of beer and ran quickly into the road. He raised the bottle carefully and bashed Steve's attacker on the head with it. Ginger went down to his hands and knees and the Old Man kicked him.

The two lodgers had never seen such a fight and they ran up and down like rabbits trying to stop it. It was too late. They didn't realise, as I did, that my family actually enjoyed a good scrap. I ran over to the sweet-shop where Tim's opponent was sliding to the ground again.

'And a happy Christmas to you, mate,' said Tim, and he hit him for the last time.

'Watch out, Tim,' I said. 'A couple of coppers just looked out of the nick.'

Lavender Hill Police Station is on the corner of Latchmere Road, no distance from where the fight was taking place. I hadn't seen any policemen but I thought it was a good idea to get back to the turkey before it burnt. Tim gave the warning whistle that we always used as a family and we picked up our bottles and ran up the road.

I was indoors before the others, running ahead to get the dinner out of the oven and onto the plates. Behind me, coming up the street, they were shouting and laughing with triumph, as if they'd pushed the North Koreans back over the Yalu River all on their own.

They were wounded and sore but they bathed their knuckles and bruises and recounted the details of the fight ten times over: how Tim had picked his man up from the ground and given him double his share, how the Old Man had saved Steve and how Joe had knocked his fellow unconscious. They laughed at the lodgers too for trying to stop a fight, making them feel ashamed they hadn't joined in.

We hadn't lost one bottle in the scrimmage. Even the one my Old Man had used as a club was drinkable, though it erupted when it was opened and drenched the table. That only made us laugh the more and we pulled the crackers and put on the paper hats.

'There's no holding us when we get going,' said the Old Man and he looked proudly at his sons, even me.

It was stupid and I knew it, but I felt my heart expanding against my ribs and for a moment I loved them all, even my father.

It took me a long while to find out how the fight had begun. It seems that on the way back from the Junction Steve, who moved very slowly, had lagged behind the others and had been overtaken by another large group of men. One of them, seeing him on his own, had made some remarks about Juno and the kids, and Steve, not thinking, not caring perhaps, had spun round with surprising agility and knocked the offender down, breaking his jaw with one blow. There had been no Christmas dinner for him that day.

Steve had been immediately surrounded and attacked by the man's friends. Fortunately Tim had looked behind him to see what had become of his brother and had seen the beginning of the fight. Calling to the others, Tim stood his bottles on the pavement, told the Old Man to look after them, and, wahooing like the US Cavalry, set off to the rescue, closely followed by Ned and Joe. They had no idea what had started the scrap but they certainly weren't going to allow one of their own to be beaten while they stood watching.

It was the best running fight I'd ever witnessed, but I was pleased my mother would never know we'd been fighting over Juno, and on Christmas Day too.

After dinner they fell asleep and snored on the sofa and in the armchairs and Bernard came along as he'd promised. He was out of uniform, but his shorter hair made him look strange and he stood straighter and he'd put on weight. He could still make me laugh as easily; he took one look at my family sleeping here and there, mouths open, black-eyed and bruised, and said, 'If they sent your lot to Korea the war would be over in a week.'

Bernard spent all his leave with me and one day I took some money from the house-keeping and we went to Bournemouth to see my mother. It was a good journey, we sat in the restaurant car like business-men and stretched our legs and talked like we'd always talked. Bernard had been taken into the artillery, but at the end of his preliminary training he'd become a projectionist again, showing films to troops up and down the country. He was bored with it, but it was better to be bored to death as a projectionist than blown to bits as a bombardier. National Servicemen were being posted to Korea and quite a few had been killed. At least in Bernard's job there was little or no chance of being sent over to fight, which pleased us both because the war was becoming fiercer week by week.

Bernard talked a lot in the restaurant car and I began to see how much he thought of my mother. His own parents had nagged him hard, cramming his every minute with sharp-edged words. His mother had often refused to do his washing, refused sometimes to have him in the house. My Ma had always laughed when Bernard had felt sorry for himself and during our time in the Gardens she had told him to throw his shirts in the dirty pile with ours. Gradually Bernard had become one of the family, wandering in and out of the flat with the same ease as the rest of us; my mother's over-worked and exploited love had found Bernard and taken him in as well as his washing.

As I listened to Bernard I began to gather up all I knew of her: her stories, her songs, her fights, her runnings away. Some time in the future, I thought, I would have to plait each weak thread of memory to another, until I had cords strong enough to bind my mother to me, to stop her slipping away.

She had been words to me at first—the stories of her childhood, her father, the Great War; words in a private voice, a voice that knew more than I was ever likely to know. I didn't notice my mother's face until I had been listening to the words for years, not until that day when she had carried me home from the nursery and my brothers were baptised. High up above the pavement I had turned my head to find my mother laughing at me. I had been surprised. Why hadn't I looked at this face before when it was so beautiful, how had I come to miss it in the first four–five long years of life? Ma had laughed again, in spite of the shopping bags and the weight of me, she had laughed and talked all the way home and I had gazed at her, sneering with pity at the other dwellers of Battersea who didn't have such a mother in their families. She'd hoisted me up in a succession of jolts, to fork my legs across her hip, making me easier to carry, and that day, up near her shoulder, I'd put my arm around her neck and everything had been all right.

But her kindness was lined with a mocking sense of humour, humour that was motivated by a concern for her children. She would never allow us to move ourselves into the centre of the world. Complain of the smell of the dustbin in the kitchen and she told you that your nose was too near your mouth. Lack energy and what you wanted was 'backbone, not wishbone.' Become pretentious and she'd remind you that 'Your arse wasn't hung with diamonds,' or 'Nobody farts incense, nobody.'

How had she borne up under it all? Deserted like that, nagged and pursued up and down and across London by debt and tiredness, always so tired, her legs aching from standing behind tables, running from kitchen to restaurant, pushing the doors with her feet, hot plates balanced on hands, wrists and elbows, swaying herself along corridors. And at night bringing home contraband beef in mouth-stained napkins. Tired, yet still saving something of herself for herself, secret. However beaten down by work, she filled in her football pools and read far into each night and hoped, her library books stacked high on a bedside chair. In the dark, on my way to the lavatory, how many times had I seen the line of light under her door where I knew she lay awake, alone, a book in her hand, a soup-plate full of dog-ends, dreaming her dreams. Once she had a book she'd stay with it until she'd fallen asleep sitting upright. In the morning she'd take it off to work with her, half-hating it for making her so tired, but reading in the bus-queue just the same, and on the top-deck, peering through the moist smoke that poured from other people's lungs.

Bernard was shocked when he saw her at Bourne-mouth, he hadn't seen her since his call-up. Ma smiled when we walked in and I saw that she'd come to love Bernard as much as he loved her—as if she didn't have enough people to love! Bernard hardly recognised the thin face and the big round eyes which made the head so sad and small. I saw the big dry lump come up his throat and I watched him swallow it.

The convalescent home was very restful, more like a hotel in nice grounds than a hospital. We pretended to be cheery and told her a few jokes and stories and I insisted that she wasn't to worry about the flat or the bills. She seemed content, but wanted to come home to be with Evie.

When she said goodbye to Bernard she did it very carefully, as if she thought she wouldn't see him again. I think it was her certainty that she wouldn't last until his next leave that broke us up more than anything else. She patted his hand and said, 'You be careful, Bern, you be careful. Keep your head down. The first war killed my dad, the second nearly did for Steve, as good as . . . We don't want you messed up, do we? After all, you're one of the family, you know.'

We felt pretty miserable leaving her, our silly presents on her bed. What can you do when someone looks that ill, that tired? What had she got out of life but hard times and hard knocks? When you asked her she always said that her kids had made her life worthwhile. I found that hard to swallow; she'd got precious little out of us.

I walked along the front with Bernard at Bournemouth and we talked it up and down. It was a trap and we were stuck with it. We stood and looked at the sea and Bernard said, 'We all got to die some day, it's a bastard, ain't it?'

We caught the train to London and Bernard went back to his barracks. I only saw him once more that winter, during a brief embarkation leave before he was sent to Korea to show films to the troops.

The kick on the head at Christmas hadn't done Steve any good. Every day he deteriorated. He only got up to go to the lavatory. He wouldn't face anyone and would talk only to me. Once every seven days he went out and crept, close to the walls, down to the Labour Exchange for his money, and on the way home spent it in an off-licence. The rest of the week he stayed in his bedroom either asleep or drunk. I could see him growing fatter by the day. He was sweaty, unclean.

I kept him hidden, I shared his shame as I had shared his glory. I told him when the lodgers were out so he could cross the hall to the bathroom unseen. I kept the key out of the front door and in my pocket so that Juno could not get at him. She'd tried to get past me a couple of times but I'd kept the chain on the door and never let her through.

One day she beat me; she was a determined woman. I'd gone downstairs to leave the dustbin on the step and left the front door open. I didn't see her slip behind me, nor did I hear her run up the stairs. I had no idea she was there as I went back, until I heard her voice in

Steve's bedroom shouting, 'Look at yer, look at yer, you poor ol' man ... How are the mighty fallen!' Her voice was hard and stretched.

I ran up the stairs, into the flat and round to Steve's room. Juno was standing in the doorway, holding onto it, she had one foot on the bed and was shoving hard with it, spiking her stiletto heel into Steve's stomach. Her face muscles were tight with hatred, her lips rolling over her teeth, horse-like.

For all her shouting and screaming Steve took no notice; he might have been asleep or drugged. His eyes were open but he looked through Juno, through the wall of the bedroom. For him she wasn't there.

But she was for me. I couldn't bear to see her doing this to Steve. Whatever he was now I remembered what he had been.

I seized her arm and attempted to pull her out of the doorway. It was not easy; she was big, strong as a navvy. She held onto the jamb with one hand and I couldn't budge her. I slammed the door; it should have cut her hand in two but she hardly noticed it. I jostled her into the hall, grasped her round the neck and pulled her forward. Her arms and hands were beating and scratching, her feet were kicking at me and her face, close to mine, was shouting, shouting. The whites of her eyes rolled and spit was lying thick along her lips.

I shut Steve's door with one hand but she got her knee into my crutch and squirmed it hard in. It hurt. I used my weight to fall on top of her and we both went over onto the floor. She let her body go limp underneath me, I could feel her breasts moving under my hands, alive. Her arms went round my neck and pulled my head down and her mouth was all over mine, hard, soft, tongue searching under my tongue, the taste of gin on it. She bit my lips and her long strong legs were round me and her pelvis grabbed and dragged me into her. I had never known anything so powerful. Every bone she had was articulated and could hold me. I understood now why men wanted her. My body went with hers, my arms went round her, I kissed her. I felt her hand move to my belt, I helped it, it was inside now and gripped me hard. I undid my clothes and helped her undo hers.

It was too much for me and I came over the front of her dress. The decision had not been mine, but at least I hadn't done it with her, with Steve in the next room listening to the noise and staring through the wall.

I rolled over, got to my knees and fastened my trousers. Juno rose to her feet, her legs straight and tense. She pushed me over with her foot.

'You little pansy!' she said. 'Like getting marshmallow through a key-hole that was,' and she laughed at her own obscenity and rattled down the stairs, still laughing. I heard her evil high-heels stabbing at the pavement all the way down the road.

I turned the radio on loud and went into Steve's room to steal some of his drink. He had rolled over and was looking at the other wall, away from the door. I didn't know if he was awake or not. I took the whisky and went into the living-room and drank it until I was drunk and could fall asleep.

Whenever I could I still went, in the middle of the night, to see Bungey in the Savoy accounts office and he ordered coffee and sandwiches from the kitchens. I never stayed more than an hour or so because he had his columns of figures to add up. I began to suspect that Bungey talked over my head for his own amusement, to confuse too. Perhaps he had always meant to confuse. I decided it didn't matter, I had to talk to someone who knew the things I didn't. I wanted desperately to know what to do. I agreed with Bungey that the doing of things was easy, it was even easy to excel if you set your mind to it, but the great difficulty was deciding what it was you wanted to excel at. And when you'd chosen, had you got it right or wrong?

Bungey himself had worked at many things, moved all over London with all manner of people, but he wasn't doing what he wanted. He wanted to finish the poetry he was always starting, and he wanted it to be good, so good that everyone knew it. I could see it clearly. The obsession animated his whole life, like I knew his body, never seen, was the thing that held his immaculate and threadbare suit in an upright position and made it move when he walked or danced. Yet, strong as his obsession was, part of him seemed to hold back, hesitating to complete what he began, as if he had decided that really there was nothing worth doing.

But I talked to him of other things and even if he did smile at me ironically and was sometimes urbane to the point of brittleness I was still convinced that he was kind and, as my mother would have said, 'His heart's in the right place, and that's the most important thing, always has been, don't you forget it.'

We talked often of the news from Korea because Bernard was there. We talked a lot about war in general because there had been so many and we'd seen two. 'Amazing how they keep coming back,' Bungey said, 'and how we let them when they do.'

It was at the Savoy that I discovered that Bungey had been a conscientious objector during World War Two. They'd made him join the Friends' Ambulance Unit and he'd spent months at Belsen and Dachau, clearing up.

At the end of the war they'd shown films of the extermination camps and they'd let us kids in to watch; so we wouldn't forget I suppose. I remember: bulldozers moving mountains of white bodies, a mess of limbs and heads, corpses rolling, stiff-armed, over and over into huge pits. I'd seen close-ups of the survivors as they crawled out of the prison huts, their skin tight to their bones, their eyes soft and hurt like beaten dogs. I woke up in terror at night, my child's nightmare of the green dragon on its yellow plain banished for ever. If Belsen had frightened me for life in the dark of the cinema, what had it done to Bungey in the full light of day, with the stench ready and warm in his nostrils and the arms turning over like the spokes of broken wheels on their way to the burial pits?

'You know,' said Bungey, 'when I'd finished at Belsen I wondered if anything was worth anything, even not fighting.'

They let my mother out in March and I made the flat as tidy as I could. When I went to fetch her she seemed more like her old self, but she was still frail. I wondered how she would react when she saw what Steve had become. I tried to tell her in the train how ill he was.

'I'm not surprised,' she said.

When we reached the flat she walked into his room and looked at him. I'd kept it orderly but there was no mistaking what had happened to Steve, there was no tidying that away. She bit her mouth and looked round the walls.

Steve said, 'Hello, Mum,' in the pathetic little voice he'd taken to talking in, and stared at the window.

My mother sunk a deep breath and went into the living-room and sat down, and I made a pot of tea.

She didn't like the lodger set-up and wanted to go back to work. I argued strongly against it. I thought it would be better for her to let things stay as they were for a while, she wouldn't get so tired. I promised to find a job as soon as I could; she needn't worry, she could have a holiday in the summer.

I began looking for work the next day but was relieved when no one would take me on because I was too close to my National Service. I let it slide; we had enough money to live on anyway and Ma seemed to want me at home. It was a special quiet period for both of us. We kept a long conversation going, day in, day out, and we laughed at each other, doing odd jobs, painting the walls. We went to the cinema, even the theatre a couple of times, and we became friends, sharing most of our thoughts, all of them really except the most secret ones.

After Easter, one Monday evening, there was a banging at the street door. I leapt up because I thought it might be Juno again. I ran to the door, ready this time, and threw it open.

Bernard's mother stood on the dark landing, her peculiar little white face swaying on her shoulders. I hadn't realised she knew where we lived; she had always considered herself a cut above us.

She had a letter in her hand, her mouth was open and not a sound came out of it. She waved her arms at me. I looked at her; she'd gone mad. There were tears on her face; her mouth closed, opened again. Then I knew and knew it for certain and I felt it going into my blood, cold . . . I knew that Bernard was dead.

I snatched the letter from her and stepped back into the light. I saw the heading on the notepaper, the regimentals, and the signature of the officer, and I read

a sentence that told how popular Bernard had been.
Been! The shell had wiped out the whole cinema.

My mother had followed me into the hall. I turned
and threw myself in her arms and the tears came and
she took me back into the living-room. There was the
table and the chairs and the cups and they all looked
evil. Everything I knew, the street, the houses, the
shops, would all be there tomorrow, trying to look the
same as before, but they wouldn't, they would still look
evil; they were there and Bernard wasn't. And people
too, idiots in pubs, picking up pints, alive when Bernard
was dead.

I couldn't speak for crying, or breathe, my nose and
mouth were blocked. Bernard's mother followed us in,
sobbing, looking round the room as if she wanted to get
out but had forgotten where the door was. She screwed
her fists into her stomach to hold it in. I had to walk
about from room to room. I couldn't look at anything
without crying because I could think of nothing else
but Bernard, dead. There was no squirming round that
one thought, it was the only thought in the world.

My mother was sitting on the sofa with her arms
round Bernard's mother, talking for the sake of talking,
about her own father, how he'd been shot in no-man's
land, about when she'd been a girl. It made me angry
to see her so composed; didn't she ever lose her temper
with it, didn't she want to shout against it all? I bawled
at her, 'What am I to do, eh? Sit around here so they
can come and get me, tell me what to do, order me
about, make me a Hucker for the rest of my life?
They're not getting me, army or navy, I'm damned if
I'll do what they want, damned.' I left the room again,
wheeling through the flat. I went into my bedroom and
began to put things into a holdall, crying, not seeing
what I was doing. By the time I got back to the living-

room my mother was making tea. She had taken
control again, for the first time since her illness, and in
a way I was glad, but her calmness still angered me.

I watched the tea brewed. All her years seemed to
inform the ritual and showed me how impressive was
the way she accepted her existence, and in the same
moment I saw the hopelessness of it all. My blood rose.

'Come on, Mick,' she said, ignoring my holdall, 'have
some tea, do you good.'

The thought of tea, anything, disgusted me; so much
eating, drinking, peeing, crapping, and Bernard dead.

'Ma,' I said, 'I'm not hanging about on the Hill for
those sods to get me. Apart from you there's nothing to
keep me here. I'm going, and when the call-up papers
come you can send them back and say I've gone, you
don't know where, which will be true because I don't
know either. I'll come and see you though, a lot, I will.'

I didn't want to leave her on her own, but I had to.
She was good about it, what else, and said, 'Yes, yes,
you just take care. Come and see me when you can,
we'll be all right,' and she gave Bernard's mother a
squeeze. I walked out before my temper slipped beyond
control and left them on the sofa with their tea.

I couldn't get on a bus, my face was red and swollen
and I could hardly see. I walked down Latchmere
Road because I thought I'd go to Bungey's; then I
remembered that he was at work, so I phoned him.

He found it difficult to understand what I was saying
at first. I couldn't explain without crying and sniffing
and blowing my nose. When he understood I heard
him move his hand over the receiver, but it must have
been only one sob that got away from him because he
came straight back and his voice was steady. He'd seen
a lot of death.

He said that I could stay with him and Jennifer until

I sorted myself out. I was to go to his place; he'd phone and tell her I was coming and he'd leave work early to come home and talk to me.

I left the telephone-box and walked all the way up Albert Bridge Road. I broke down again along there because the road took me past the Park gates that Bernard and I had gone through every day we'd been at the Gardens. When it came to crossing the river I thought I'd never make it. Albert Bridge was the one we'd peed off, our biggest laugh ever, the night with the two manageresses. I took a deep breath and kept going. The wind beat across the river and across my eyes, roaring into my ears. Passers-by stared at me, but I tucked my head down and ran, not hesitating once, not looking behind or down into the water.

On the far side I stopped. I placed the holdall on the parapet and leant against it and wiped my eyes. There was nothing more to come, I was empty, dry. I looked up. Battersea Park was black, the black trees moved against a black sky. I shoved my head against my holdall and howled silently at the dirty river for my dead friend. My anger spun and leapt up in me. I wanted revenge, revenge for the summer's broken promises. I wanted everyone to know how promises were broken and I wanted to be the one to tell them; why should I acquiesce and keep silent?

But I didn't have the words and didn't know where to get them. Bungey did. Perhaps he could finish a poem for once, if he had the callousness to do it. He must have. Hadn't his interest in Bernard and me been callous? Hadn't he been watching us, spying on us, and weren't we all the same? We all fed from living bits of other people, survived on them, grew on them. I felt the hate in me rise up in my throat, rising up for my brothers and my father and the slow wearing down of my mother. But I saw too that she knew about that much better than I did and accepted it. She was alone with Steve and Evie now and still she would take this latest hurt to herself and fold it away inside her in silence.

I saw all that and still I had to go, to escape from what the Huckers had in store for me if I were fool enough to wait for them in one place. I wouldn't let them force me to live the kind of life they had planned. Since I could do nothing else I would do what I wanted only. I would be selfish too, I would enjoy every minute I could and I would start right away; I had to, I couldn't trust life until tomorrow, that might be too late.

Everyone put their faith in the future but the future was faithless. My mother had given everything in the hope that her kids would be all right the next day or the day after. All she'd had in return had been sorrow. I looked again into the blackness and saw her waiting for Evie to leave home, watching Steve die maybe, feeling the sorrow rotting inside her, and we other sons doing nothing to stop that sorrow, or even ease it or slow it down. Little by little she would see less and less of us and then she would die, between one day and the next, with us away, too busy to be there. She would die in a small bed in a corner, alone, apologetically, one foot on the floor, trying to get to the bathroom, not wishing to embarrass anyone, and under her pillow we would find the money for her funeral with a few quid over so we could have a drink and a row afterwards.